GCSE English

Lord of the Flies

by William Golding

It may be set on a sun-kissed tropical island, but *Lord of the Flies* is darker than a Year 7 geography field trip to the Wookey Hole Caves.

Luckily, this fantastic CGP Workbook is here to shed some light. It's brimming with practice questions to test you on the plot, characters, themes, context and more — and we've included brilliant essay-writing practice too.

When CGP offers you all this, choosing anyone else's *Lord of the Flies* Workbook would just be pig-headed...

The Workbook

Contents

CONTENTS

Published by CGP

Editors:
Claire Boulter
Emma Cleasby
Rose Jones
Louise McEvoy
Jack Perry
James Summersgill

With thanks to Izzy Bowen and Nicola Woodfin for the proofreading.
With thanks to Jan Greenway for the copyright research.

Acknowledgements:

With thanks to Lilith Antinori & John Stanmeyer/National Geographic Creative for permission to use the front cover image.

With thanks to Photostage for permission to use the images on pages 1 and 22.

With thanks to Rex Features for permission to use the images on pages 3, 11, 28 and 32.

With thanks to Alamy for permission to use the images on pages 4, 8, 16, 30 and 38.

With thanks to ArenaPAL for permission to use the images on pages 6, 13, 17, 18, 19, 20, 21, 26 and 36.

ISBN: 978 1 78294 782 0

Printed by Elanders Ltd, Newcastle upon Tyne.

Clipart from Corel®

Based on the classic CGP style created by Richard Parsons.

How to Use this Book

Practise the four main skills you'll need for the exam

Each question tests <u>one or more</u> of the <u>four skills</u> you'll be tested on in the <u>exam</u>. You'll need to:

1) Write about the text in a <u>thoughtful way</u>, <u>picking out</u> appropriate <u>examples</u> and <u>quotations</u> to back up your opinions.

2) <u>Identify</u> and <u>explain</u> features of the book's <u>form</u>, <u>structure</u> and <u>language</u>. Using <u>subject terminology</u>, show how the author uses these to create <u>characters</u> and <u>settings</u>, explore <u>themes</u> and affect the <u>reader's reactions</u>.

3) Write about the book's <u>context</u>.

4) Write in a <u>clear</u>, <u>well-structured</u> and <u>accurate</u> way. <u>5%</u> of the marks in your English Literature GCSE are for <u>spelling</u>, <u>punctuation</u> and <u>grammar</u>.

Most exam boards will want you write about context. Ask your teacher if you're not sure.

Use this workbook with or without the CGP Text Guide

1) This workbook is perfect to use with CGP's <u>Text Guide</u> for *Lord of the Flies*. The workbook matches <u>each section</u> of the Text Guide, so you can test your knowledge <u>bit by bit</u>.

2) You can also use this book <u>by itself</u>. It covers all the <u>important</u> parts of the text — <u>plot</u>, <u>characters</u>, <u>context</u>, <u>themes</u> and the <u>writer's techniques</u>.

3) The questions refer to the text <u>in detail</u> — you'll need a <u>copy</u> of the novel to make the most of the workbook.

© Donald Cooper/photostage

It prepares you for the exam every step of the way

1) The exam section is jam-packed with <u>useful advice</u>. It <u>guides</u> you through how to tackle the exam, from understanding the questions to building great answers. There's also an easy-to-read <u>mark scheme</u>, which you can use to mark <u>sample answers</u> and improve answers of your <u>own</u>.

2) There are four pages of <u>practice exam questions</u> spread across the book. They give you the opportunity to use what you've revised in each section to write a <u>realistic answer</u>.

3) <u>Exam tips</u> and extra <u>practice exam questions</u> are included throughout the book. There are also helpful <u>revision tasks</u> designed to get you thinking more creatively. These are marked with <u>stamps</u>.

4) You can find <u>answers</u> to all of the <u>questions</u> and <u>tasks</u> at the back of the book.

5) Each section contains at least one 'Skills Focus' page. These pages help you to practise important skills <u>individually</u>. You can tackle them in <u>any order</u> and prioritise the skills you find the <u>hardest</u>.

I bet you're conch-ously looking forward to reading on...

Now you've got to grips with the essentials of how to use this book, you're ready to enter the big wide world of workbook questions. All you need is a pen, a copy of the novel and a snack of choice for the road... mmm...

Chapter One — The Sound of the Shell

The boys gather together after a plane crash

Q1 Read Chapter One from "**The shore was fledged**" to "**the dazzling beach and the water**".
What impression do you get of the island in this passage? Give a reason for your answer.

....

....

....

Q2 Decide whether each statement is **true** or **false**, then find a short quote to support each answer.

a) Ralph is kind to Piggy. **True:** ☐ **False:** ☐

Quote: ....

b) Piggy worries that they may be trapped on the island for a long time. **True:** ☐ **False:** ☐

Quote: ....

c) Jack bosses the choirboys around. **True:** ☐ **False:** ☐

Quote: ....

Q3 'The fact that the boys elect a chief shows that they are civilised at this point
in the story'. Do you agree with this statement? Explain your answer.

....

....

....

Q4 Why do you think Jack hesitates to kill the piglet? Use a quote to support your answer.

....

....

....

Sucks to your C sharp, Jack — Ralph can play the conch...

Although Ralph and Jack seem friendly to each other, the vote causes the first conflict within the group.
Write a paragraph on who you'd vote for as leader and why, using evidence from Chapter One.

   ☐   ☐   ☐

Chapter Two — Fire on the Mountain

The boys build a fire that gets out of control

Q1 Put these events in order by numbering the boxes.
The first one has been done for you.

A littlun says he saw a creature in the night. ☐

A rule is made that only the person holding the conch can speak. ☐

Piggy realises that one of the littluns is missing. ☐

Ralph blows the conch to call another meeting. ☐ 1

Some of the boys climb the mountain to light a signal fire. ☐

Jack thinks the boys need an army to hunt pigs. ☐

© Alastair Muir/REX/Shutterstock

Q2 Why does Ralph get frustrated with the littluns during the assembly in this chapter?

....

....

Q3 Answer each question and then choose a quote from the text that supports your answer.

a) How does Ralph feel about the fact that he doesn't know how to light a fire?

....

Quote: ....

b) What does Piggy think of the rule about holding the conch to speak?

....

Quote: ....

Q4 Read from "**The crowd was as silent as death**" to the end of the chapter. How does the description of the setting hint that the boy with the mulberry birthmark dies in the fire?

....

....

....

They're all a bit harsh to Piggy — bunch of swines...

MAKING LINKS

Write a paragraph explaining how Golding makes Chapter Two seem more tense than Chapter One.
Include a couple of quotes to support your answer — the shorter and more memorable, the better.

 ☐ ☐ ☐

Section One — Analysis of Chapters

Chapter Three — Huts on the Beach

The boys stop working as a group

Q1 Read from "**Jack was bent double**" to "**brushed it with their bristly hide.**"
What impression do you get of the forest in this passage? Use a quote to support your answer.

....

....

Q2 Find a quote to support each of the statements below.

a) Ralph is doubtful that the shelters will ever be finished.

Quote: ....

b) Jack suggests that he understands the littluns' fear.

Quote: ....

© Columbia/courtesy Everett
Collection Inc / Alamy Stock Photo

Q3 Towards the end of Chapter Three, Ralph and Jack look at each other "**baffled, in love and hate**". Explain what this suggests about their relationship at this point in the novel.

....

....

....

Q4 Complete the passage below using words from the box. Each gap should have a different word.

.... walks into the forest alone, then crawls into a small, quiet space. This shows

that he enjoys being .... by nature. The way he .... himself from

the other boys suggests he is .... from them. The description of the sights and

sounds of the island gives the end of the chapter an almost .... feel.

| surrounded | sorrowful | Ralph | isolates | safe | magical | changed | protects | Simon | different |

Beach huts — for when a stripy windbreak just won't do....

The division between the builders and the hunters becomes clearer in this chapter. Jot down which
characters are in which group, then summarise each group's beliefs and how the groups are presented.

Chapter Four — Painted Faces and Long Hair

The boys have a chance of rescue — but the fire has gone out

Q1 Read from "**Roger and Maurice came out of the forest**" to "**invisible arrows.**" Decide whether these statements are **true** or **false**.

	True	False
Roger is reluctant to destroy the littluns' sandcastles.	☐	☐
Maurice feels guilty for getting sand in Percival's eye.	☐	☐
The littluns comfort each other.	☐	☐
Henry enjoys having power over the creatures he finds on the shore.	☐	☐

Q2 In Chapter Four, Roger starts throwing stones around Henry.
Why do you think Golding included this event in the novel?

....

....

....

Q3 How does Jack's character change immediately after painting the mask on his face?

....

....

....

Q4 Find a quote to back up each of these statements.

a) Ralph is cross that the fire was left unattended and had gone out.

....

b) Piggy is furious with Jack for going hunting.

....

c) Ralph stands up for Piggy when Jack breaks his glasses.

....

Henry was close by — a stone's throw from Roger, in fact...

You'll need to use examples from the novel as evidence in the exam. That's where having a really good understanding of the plot comes in useful — make sure you know what happens and when.

 ☐   ☐   ☐

Chapter Five — Beast from Water

Ralph realises things are going wrong

Q1 Read from **"Ralph turned to the chief's seat"** to **"put the conch to his lips."**
What does the reader learn about Ralph's attitude towards Piggy in this passage?

....

....

....

Q2 Many of the boys continue to believe that the beast exists, despite the fact
that no sightings of it have been confirmed. Why do you think this is?

....

....

Q3 Identify who says each of these phrases, then explain what it shows about how they are feeling.

a) **"What's grown-ups going to think?"**   Said by: ....

Shows that: ....

b) **"Fat lot of good we are"**   Said by: ....

Shows that: ....

Q4 How does Golding show that Ralph is losing his authority as
chief in this chapter? Use a quote to support your answer.

....

....

....

....

© Johan Persson/ArenaPAL

PRACTICE
TASK

Ralph's lack of authority was chief among the problems...

Imagine you've been observing the boys on the island. Look back over the novel so far and write a
few notes about your findings — include things they've done well, and anything you'd do differently.

Chapter Six — Beast from Air

The body of a dead airman lands on the island

Q1 Why do you think Golding places the description of the airman falling onto the island at the start of the chapter?

....

....

Q2 State how the following characters react to Sam and Eric's claim that they've seen the beast. Give a quote to support each answer.

a) Piggy: ....

Quote: ....

b) Ralph: ....

Quote: ....

c) Simon: ....

Quote: ....

Q3 When the older boys are on the way to find the beast, Ralph feels a sense of dread. What is he dreading? Use a quote to back up your answer.

....

....

Q4 Explain how Golding makes Castle Rock seem like a threatening place in this chapter.

....

....

....

....

The only beast you'll have to take down is the exam...

...so keep revising and it should be a clean kill. As you're going through the book you should be writing down short, snappy quotes to learn — you'll need to use quotes to pick up marks in the exam.

Chapter Seven — Shadows and Tall Trees

Some of the boys go up the mountain in search of the beast

Q1   Put these events in order by numbering the boxes. The first one has been done for you.

Simon says that Ralph will return home one day. ☐

Ralph feels helpless looking out to sea. ☐ 1

Ralph and the other boys try to kill a boar. ☐

Ralph mistakes the dead airman for the beast. ☐

The boys hurt Robert, who is pretending to be a pig. ☐

Ralph thinks about his old home in England. ☐

© Columbia/courtesy Everett
Collection Inc / Alamy Stock Photo

Q2   How does Jack react to Ralph wounding a boar in this chapter? Why does he react in this way?

....

....

....

Q3   Read from "**Ralph turned back to Jack**" to "**the two started up the mountain.**" What motivates Ralph and Jack to climb the mountain in this passage? Use a quote to back up your answer.

....

....

....

Q4   How does the way Golding describes the island in this chapter contrast with the way it is described in Chapter One? What does this contrast suggest?

....

....

....

....

Another task, but don't worry — it's just a littlun...

During this chapter, the littluns are left behind while Ralph, Jack and Roger search for the beast.
Write a few sentences about how well you think the littluns have been looked after up to this point.

 ☐   ☐ ☺ ☐

Chapter Eight — Gift for the Darkness

Jack tries to take over as chief and forms a new group

Q1 Jack tries to take power by making the other boys see Ralph in a negative light.
Explain how he does this, using a quote to support your answer.

....

....

....

Q2 Decide whether each of the following statements is **true** or **false**.
For each one, find a quote to support your answer.

    a) Piggy thinks it will be impossible for them to survive without Jack.   **True:** ☐   **False:** ☐

    Quote: ....

    b) The boys in Ralph's group are reluctant to build a new fire.   **True:** ☐   **False:** ☐

    Quote: ....

    c) Some boys sneak off to join Jack's tribe.   **True:** ☐   **False:** ☐

    Quote: ....

Q3 After Jack puts the pig's head on a stick, calling it "**a gift**" for the
beast, the boys run away. Explain why you think they do this.

....

....

Q4 Read from "**You are a silly little boy**" to the end of the chapter. What message
does Golding convey to the reader in this passage? Explain your answer.

....

....

....

If someone gave me a hog's head I'd be pigged off...

The split in the group after the vote is one of the most important moments in the novel. Write a short
paragraph from Jack's point of view, explaining how he feels about it, then do the same for Ralph.

 ☐   ☐   ☐   **Section One — Analysis of Chapters**

Chapter Nine — A View to a Death

The tribe murders Simon

Q1 How does the weather change from the start of the chapter up until Simon's death? What effect does this have on the atmosphere of the chapter?

....

....

....

Q2 Read from "**At last he turned away**" to "**Jack waved his spear again.**"
Find a quote to support each of the following statements.

a) Simon realises that the beast can't hurt the boys.

Quote: ....

b) The tribe treats Jack like a god.

Quote: ....

c) Ralph and Piggy are grateful for the food offered to them by Jack's tribe.

Quote: ....

Q3 What does Golding suggest about Jack's power when he says that it "**lay in the brown swell of his forearms**"?

....

Q4 How does Golding make the boys' murder of Simon seem savage? Support your answer with a quote.

....

....

....

....

 And I thought savage behaviour was eating the last sweet...

After Simon's death, the mood of the chapter changes dramatically. Write a paragraph describing how the mood is different and explaining why Golding might have wanted to end the chapter in this way.

Section One — Analysis of Chapters

Chapter Ten — The Shell and the Glasses

Jack's tribe steal Piggy's glasses

Q1 Read from "**At length Ralph got up**" to "**We left early.**"
Decide whether these statements are **true** or **false**.

	True	False
Ralph thinks he should call another assembly.	☐	☐
Piggy suggests that Simon was to blame for his own death.	☐	☐
Ralph was on the outside of the circle when Simon was killed.	☐	☐
Sam and Eric weren't at the dance when Simon was killed.	☐	☐

Q2 Read from "**A log had been jammed**" to "**the savages murmured again**", then answer the following questions.

    a) How do you think Robert feels about Jack? Refer to the passage in your answer.

....

....

    b) Why do you think Jack refuses to admit that the 'beast' has been killed?

....

....

Q3 At first, Ralph and Piggy think that Jack's tribe might have attacked them to steal the conch. Why did they initially think that the tribe wanted the conch?

....

....

Q4 Why has Jack become "**a chief now in truth**" by the end of the chapter?

....

....

MAKING LINKS

I guess you could say Ralph and Piggy were hambushed...

Lord of the Flies shows how a group of people slowly starts to break apart, so it's no use just looking at each chapter in isolation — think about how events earlier in the novel lead to what happens later on.

 ☐   ☐   ☐

Chapter Eleven — Castle Rock

Piggy is killed at Castle Rock

Q1   Read from "**He'll be painted**" to "**Piggy spoke, kindly**". Explain why the characters disagree about the idea of disguising themselves.

....

....

....

Q2   Decide whether each statement is **true** or **false**, and find a quote to support your answer.

a) The tribe takes Ralph's demand for Piggy's glasses seriously.　　**True:** ☐　**False:** ☐

Quote: ....

b) Ralph is impressed by the fire that Jack's tribe has made.　　**True:** ☐　**False:** ☐

Quote: ....

c) Piggy still believes that the conch holds power.　　**True:** ☐　**False:** ☐

Quote: ....

Q3   Explain how the way Piggy is murdered affects the reader's opinion of Jack's tribe.

....

....

....

Q4   Read from "**This time the silence**" to the end of the chapter. Find a quote that shows Jack wants to kill Ralph. Explain how it shows this.

Quote: ....

Explanation: ....

....

Castle rock was always my favourite musical sub-genre...

Imagine you're a film director adapting the novel to be set somewhere other than an island, and with adult characters. Write a few lines about how you'd adapt the novel and how it might affect the plot.

      ☐   ☐   😊 ☐

Chapter Twelve — Cry of the Hunters

Ralph is in danger — but is rescued by a naval officer

Q1   Put these events in order by numbering the boxes. The first one has been done for you.

Jack's tribe launches rocks onto Ralph's hiding place. ☐

Ralph is smoked out of the thicket. ☐

Ralph tries to convince himself that Piggy's death was an accident. ☐

Ralph tries to outrun the tribe. ☐

Ralph takes the stick from the Lord of the Flies to use as a weapon. ☐

Ralph hides in some ferns close to Castle Rock. ☐ 1

Q2   In Chapter Eight, Jack tells Roger to sharpen a stick at both ends so that they can leave the pig's head on it for the beast. In Chapter Twelve, Golding reveals that Roger has "**sharpened a stick at both ends**" again. How does this make the reader fear for Ralph's safety?

....

....

....

Q3   Golding makes it seem likely that Ralph will die in the fire. Give one example of how he does this, then explain why he might have chosen to give the reader this impression.

Example: ....

Explanation: ....

....

Q4   Why do you think the naval officer is "**moved and a little embarrassed**" at the end of the novel? Explain your answer.

....

....

....

....

© Johan Persson/ArenaPAL

The boys will be rescued when pigs can fly — oh, wait...

Make a list of five events which you think have an impact on the relationship between Ralph and Jack. Then write a few sentences summarising how their relationship changes during the course of the novel.

 ☐ ☐ ☐

Using Quotes

In the exam, you'll need to use quotes from the book to back up your argument. It's worth practising this skill because your answer will be much more convincing if you can give evidence for your views. You won't have the text with you in the exam, so you'll have to learn some important quotes off by heart. This page gives you the chance to think about how to choose good quotes and use them well — have a go at the questions below and you'll soon be well on your way to exam success.

Q1 Fill in the text about how to use quotes in your answers.

A good quote is .... — you should write your quote exactly as it appears

in the text. Good quotes are also highly .... to the point being made, so

don't choose something off topic. A bad quote will be ...., and won't

support the point you're discussing. A good quote will be .... in the

sentence, rather than just added on afterwards. Only use the most ....

part of a sentence or passage — it's easier to remember short quotes. Also, a quote

shouldn't just .... your point. It should give new information.

Q2 Look at these examples and decide which use quotes well and which use them badly.

> a) Ralph realises that Piggy has "brains" and comes to respect his intelligence.
> b) Simon is presented as a kind and generous person who looks after the littluns. He is told by the Lord of the Flies that the boys "are going to have fun on this island!"
> c) Jack struggles to control his "compulsion" to kill other living things.
> d) Simon believes that the beast isn't real, as he says "What I mean is... maybe it's only us."
> e) In Chapter Four, the boys' laughter at Piggy becomes hysterical — it turns into a "gale of hysteria".

Good quote usage: ....   Bad quote usage: ....

Q3 Choose one of the examples you identified as bad in Q2 and improve it.

....

....

....

P.E.E.D.

To get a great mark, you have to do more than just comment on the text — your answer needs to be well-structured and developed. The P.E.E.D. method is a brilliant way to make sure you do this.

For each **point** you make in your answer, provide a supporting quote or a specific **example**, then **explain** how it backs up your point. Finally, **develop** your point by explaining the effect it has on the reader, or making a link with another part of the novel, a different theme or the novel's context.

Q1 None of the sample answers below have used P.E.E.D. correctly. For each, say which stage of P.E.E.D. is missing, then write a sentence you could include to improve the answer.

a)

> Jack is presented as an unpleasant character throughout the novel. He frequently belittles Piggy, telling him "Shut up, Fatty" just minutes after meeting him. Golding contrasts Jack's meanness with Ralph's fair treatment of others and respect for Piggy and his ideas.

Missing stage: .... Addition: ....

....

....

b)

> Simon is presented as an outsider by Golding. This emphasises his desire for solitude, implying that he is an outsider by choice. This contrasts with Piggy's exclusion from the group, which suggests to the reader that being an outsider is not always a negative thing.

Missing stage: .... Addition: ....

....

....

c)

> Despite being saved from the island by the naval officer, Golding suggests that the boys are not completely safe through the way the officer looks back at the "cruiser". A "cruiser" is a type of warship, so the fact that the officer glances back at it suggests that the world the characters are about to return to is dangerous.

Missing stage: .... Addition: ....

....

....

Section One — Analysis of Chapters

Ralph

Q1 Find a quote from the novel that shows that Ralph is:

a) hard-working

Quote: ....

b) decisive

Quote: ....

Q2 Fill in the gaps in the table below. The first one has been done for you.

Event in the novel	What it suggests about Ralph
a) Ralph gets frustrated that nobody wants to help build the huts.	He has different priorities to the other boys.
b) Ralph is pleased he hurt the boar.	
c) Ralph is shocked by Piggy's death.	

Q3 At the end of the novel, Ralph is "**conscious of his filthy appearance**" when he sees the naval officer. Explain what this suggests about Ralph.

....

....

Q4 In Chapter Eight, Ralph wonders "**what makes things break up**". To what extent do you think Ralph is responsible for things breaking up on the island? Explain your answer.

....

....

....

....

Ralph's a proper Brit — he's always on about the weather...

Explain how Ralph is presented as a good leader in the novel. You should write about:
*   events which show that Ralph is a good leader
*   how Ralph's leadership affects the other characters.

Piggy

Q1 Find an example in the text of Piggy behaving like an adult.
Explain what effect behaving like an adult has on Piggy's position in the group.

Example: ....

....

Explanation: ....

....

Q2 When Ralph forgets why the fire is important in Chapter Eight, Piggy "**urgently**"
reminds him that it is for "**Rescue**". What does this suggest about Piggy?

....

....

....

Q3 Look at these statements about the role of Piggy in the novel.
Decide which ones are **true** and which ones are **false**.

True **False**

Piggy highlights the other boys' irrational thinking to the reader.

Piggy makes the reader think about the 'adult' world beyond the island.

Golding shows how Piggy's intelligence challenges Ralph's leadership.

Piggy's death suggests that barbarity is stronger than civilisation.

Q4 Do you think Piggy would have made a good leader? Give reasons for your answer.

....
....
....
....
....

MAKING LINKS

Using Piggy's specs to light the fire was a glass act...

Some people think that Piggy is supposed to represent logic in the novel. Write a short paragraph
that supports this idea. Make sure you use specific examples from the text to back up your answer.

Jack

Q1 Find a quote from the novel that shows that Jack is:

a) quick-tempered

Quote: ....

b) a ruthless leader

Quote: ....

c) a bully

Quote: ....

Q2 'As a leader, Jack concentrates on ensuring that the other boys are having fun.' Do you agree with this view? Explain your answer.

....

....

....

....

Q3 In Chapter Eight, nobody votes for Jack to be chief.
What does his initial reaction to this reveal about his character?

....

....

....

Q4 When the naval officer arrives on the island, Jack thinks about saying he is the boys' leader, but then changes his mind. Why do you think he does this?

....

....

PRACTICE TASK

Jack-in-the-box — where we'd all like to see him...

Write one description of Jack's physical appearance in Chapter One and one of his appearance in Chapter Eleven. In each one, include two short quotes from the relevant chapter that describe Jack.

Simon

Q1 Read the paragraph below and fill in the gaps using words from the box.

Simon is a good-natured boy who is .... during assemblies

but is kind and .... to the littluns and other characters.

He spends a lot of time .... on the island, and seems

to have the best idea of how it is .... the boys. Some people

compare Simon to .... because of his goodness.

| helping |
| alone |
| Roger |
| timid |
| Jesus |
| playing |
| generous |
| outspoken |
| affecting |

Q2 Explain what effect Simon's fainting spells have on the reader.

© Johan Persson/ArenaPAL

....

....

....

....

Q3 Read Chapter Three from "**Simon turned away from them**" to "**susurration of the blood**".
Explain how this passage reveals Simon's perceptive nature. Use a quote to support your answer.

....

....

....

Q4 Read Chapter Nine from "**The circle became a horseshoe**" to "**over the reef and out to sea**".
How does the way that Simon's death is described affect how the reader feels about him?

....

....

....

Roger

Q1 In Chapter One, Roger is described as a "**furtive**" (secretive) boy "**who kept to himself**". How does Roger change during the course of the novel?

....

....

Q2 'In Chapter Four, Roger is presented as a civilised character.' Do you agree? Explain your answer.

© Johan Persson/ArenaPAL

....

....

....

....

....

Q3 Roger doesn't have much dialogue in the novel. How does this affect the reader's view of him?

....

....

Q4 In Chapter Ten, Roger describes Jack as a "**proper Chief**". Explain why Roger prefers Jack's leadership to Ralph's and how this affects the reader's view of Roger.

....

....

....

Q5 Why do you think Golding decided to make Roger (not Jack) kill Piggy?

....

....

PRACTICE TASK

To Roger, all's fair in love and boar...

Write a short newspaper report about Roger's role in *Lord of the Flies*. Your report should include a snappy headline, information about his wrongdoings and a few quotes about his personality.

Section Two — Characters

The Littluns

Q1 Decide whether each statement is **true** or **false**, and find a quote to back up your answer.

a) In Chapter Three, the littluns are unsettled.

True: ☐ False: ☐

Quote: ....

b) In Chapter Four, Ralph has no way to control the littluns.

True: ☐ False: ☐

Quote: ....

Q2 Find an example of an event which suggests that the older boys don't care about the littluns.

....

Q3 How do the littluns make it difficult for Ralph and Piggy to carry out their plans? Use a quote from the text to support your answer.

....

....

Q4 How does the littluns' innocence make them vulnerable? Explain your answer.

....

....

....

© Johan Persson/ArenaPAL

Q5 Explain how the littluns change during the novel, using an example from the text to support your answer.

....

....

....

....

Percival 'memory like a sieve' Wemys Madison...

MAKING LINKS

The littluns link to the theme of leadership. In Chapter One, they follow Ralph, but after Chapter Eight, they start to follow Jack because he gives them food. This shows how easily leaders can lose support.

 ☐ ☐ ☐

The Other Characters

Q1 Find a quote from the novel to back up each of the following statements about Sam and Eric.

a) They do not join Jack's tribe immediately.

Quote: ....

b) They don't like being bossed around.

Quote: ....

c) They are easily frightened.

Quote: ....

Q2 What can the reader tell about Maurice from his behaviour in Chapter Five?

....

....

Q3 Read Chapter Seven from "**Robert snarled at him**" to "**everybody laughed**". The boys follow Jack's orders even though Robert gets hurt. What does this suggest about the other boys?

....

....

Q4 Complete the table below with information about the adults in the novel.

Character	What they do in the story	Why Golding might have included them
The dead airman		
The naval officer		

Making Links

A great way to develop your answer is to make links between the points you've made and other parts of the text. For example, you could write about similar events, times when characters behave in a similar or different way or other times where a theme is presented. This page focuses on making links between the characters' actions, which will be a good recap of how and why the characters change or stay the same. Have a look back through the 'Characters' section if you need inspiration.

Q1 Fill in the table below with examples to illustrate the key points about each character. You can either use quotes or just explain what happens, as long as it's a precise example.

Character	Key Point	Example One	Example Two
Ralph	Ralph represents the theme of civilisation.		
Jack	Jack likes being in control.		
The littluns	The littluns are vulnerable.		

Q2 Now do the same for the characters below. This time, you'll need to think of your own key point about them.

Character	Key Point	Example One	Example Two
Piggy			
Roger			
Simon			

Section Two — Characters

Practice Questions

Here are some exam-style questions to get stuck into. There's quite a lot to be getting on with, so don't try to do them all at once. Find one you like the look of and jot down around five points you could write about. Then turn your plan into a full answer. Make sure you include an introduction and a conclusion.

Q1 Explain how Jack is presented as a cruel character in the novel.

Q2 In what ways is Ralph important to *Lord of the Flies*?

You should write about:
- how Ralph is presented in the novel
- what Ralph's character suggests about people more generally.

Q3 Write about the significance of the littluns in *Lord of the Flies*.

Q4 What does the relationship between Ralph and Piggy tell the reader about each of them as characters?

You should write about:
- the nature of their relationship and its development over the course of the novel
- what this shows about each of their characters.

Q5 **"Passions beat about Simon on the mountain-top with awful wings."** (Chapter Four)

Explain how Simon is presented as vulnerable in *Lord of the Flies*.

Historical Background to 'Lord of the Flies'

Q1   Read the paragraph below and fill in the gaps using the words in the box.

Golding wrote *Lord of the Flies* in the 1950s, a few years after the end of the ....

World War. Germany was led into the war by the .... Party and their leader,

Adolf Hitler. When he came to power, Hitler dismantled Germany's .... in

favour of a dictatorship, as he wanted everyone to obey him. In the war, Hitler's party

.... millions of people from Jewish and other minority groups, while

many ordinary people were too .... to do anything to stop them.

murdered democracy Hitler island bored scared Nazi First surrendered Second

Q2   In the 1930s, Adolf Hitler seized power in Germany by making promises to people
and punishing disobedience. How is this reflected in the way Jack seizes power?

....

....

....

Q3   *Lord of the Flies* was influenced by what was going on at the time it was being written.
Fill in the table with examples from the novel that reflect each of the following real-world
events. Your example could be something someone says or something that happens.

Historical event	Example in *Lord of the Flies*
a) There was widespread concern about nuclear war in the 1940s and 1950s.	
b) After World War Two, Europe was split between democracies and dictatorships.	
c) During the time of the British Empire, Britain claimed the right to govern many countries.	
d) In the 1950s, many people believed that British people were superior to others.	

 It's frankly a history where Golding got his ideas from...

It can be good to include some information about the historical background to *Lord of the Flies* in
your answer. Don't go overboard, though — make sure all context relates to the point you're making.

     Section Three — Context and Themes

Social Background to 'Lord of the Flies'

Q1 Read these statements about social class in the 1950s.
Decide whether each one is **true** or **false**.

	True	False
Most working-class people used very formal language.	☐	☐
Most working-class families couldn't afford to send their children to public schools.	☐	☐
Middle-class and upper-class children were expected to behave sensibly.	☐	☐
It was generally believed that only upper-class people were respectable.	☐	☐

Q2 Read Chapter One from "**Within the diamond haze**" to "**was set apart**".
Find a quote to back up each of the statements below.

a) The choir boys are used to a strict hierarchy.

Quote: ....

b) Piggy feels inferior to the choir.

Quote: ....

Q3 How do the actions of the boys in Chapter Nine contrast with how boys
from middle-class and upper-class backgrounds were expected to behave?

....

....

....

Q4 In the 1950s, some people believed that people from higher social
classes had a greater sense of morality than those from lower classes.
Explain how Golding shows this to be incorrect in the novel.

....

....

....

....

© Johan Persson/ArenaPAL

My social background? I have 51 followers and 45 friends...

It's useful to make links between the boys' social backgrounds and how they behave on the island.
For example, their insistence on rules early on may stem from their schooling and strict upbringing.

MAKING LINKS

 ☐ ☐ ☐

Civilisation and Barbarity

Q1 The table below includes events that show the boys behaving in a civilised way. Fill in the rest of the table with a related event that shows the boys have given in to barbarity.

Event that shows civilisation	Event that shows barbarity
a) The boys use the conch shell to call meetings.	Roger kills Piggy and destroys the conch.
b) The boys keep the fire burning in the hope of returning home.	
c) Piggy takes the boys' names when they first arrive.	

Q2 Explain how Golding uses the characters' changing appearances to symbolise their shift from civilisation to barbarity. Give examples to support your answer.

....

....

....

Q3 In Chapter Two, Jack says "**We've got to have rules**". In what ways does Jack reject this idea later in the novel? Explain your answer.

....

....

....

Q4 Read Chapter Nine from "**He ran stumbling**" to "**tearing of teeth and claws**". What do you think Golding is suggesting about barbarity in this passage? Explain your answer.

....

....

....

Those barbarians don't even eat their pizza with cutlery...

Most of the boys give in to their savage instincts. At what point in the novel do you think barbarity becomes stronger than civilisation? Write a paragraph explaining the reasons behind your choice.

Fear

Q1 In Chapter Two, the beast is described as a **"snake-thing"**. Find two quotes from elsewhere in the novel that describe the beast as a different sort of creature.

1) ....

2) ....

Q2 How does the littluns' fear of the beast affect their actions? Use a quote to support your answer.

....

....

Q3 Explain how Ralph's reaction to the littluns' fear of the beast changes over time.

....

....

Q4 In Chapter Five, Jack tells the other boys that fear can't harm them **"any more than a dream."** How is this view shown to be incorrect in the rest of the novel? Explain your answer.

....

....

....

Q5 Read Chapter Eight from "**I've called an assembly**" to "**He glowered up under his eyebrows**". How and why does Jack take advantage of the other boys' fears? Use a quote to support your answer.

....

....

....

....

I laugh in the face of fear — but I panic if I see a clown...

MAKING LINKS

Fear links to the theme of evil. As the boys become more scared, they join Jack's tribe for protection. The tribe ultimately commits the most evil actions in the book, like killing Simon in a hunting dance.

Power and Leadership

Q1 Jack takes power rather than being elected. What does this suggest about him as a leader?

....

....

Q2 Read the following statements. Which one best describes how power is presented in the novel?

Unlimited power is acceptable as long as people's basic needs are met. ☐

Rules are an important way to ensure the strong don't oppress the weak. ☐

Those with the most power are solely responsible for society working well. ☐

Q3 Find quotes to show that the following characters are only children even though they're leaders.

Jack: ....

Ralph: ....

Q4 Read Chapter Five from "**Ralph moved impatiently**" to
"**must be laid out clearly**", and then answer these questions.

a) Find a quote from this passage which suggests Ralph sometimes finds leadership difficult.

....

b) How does Golding present Ralph as a good leader in this passage?

....

....

Q5 Read Chapter Ten from "**He's going to beat Wilfred**" to "**Roger squatted with the rest.**"
Explain what this passage suggests about Golding's view of Jack's style of leadership.

....

....

....

They didn't see a boat for days — not even a leadership...

What is the significance of different leadership styles in the novel? Write an essay plan for this
question. Support your ideas with relevant examples from the text, and refer to the novel's context.

 ☐ ☐ ☐

Section Three — Context and Themes

Nature

Q1   Although the island is presented as a paradise in Chapter One, there are hints in the chapter that the island is not as perfect as it seems. Why do you think Golding does this?

© Moviestore collection Ltd / Alamy Stock Photo

....

....

....

....

....

Q2   Summarise an event in the novel which shows that nature can be dangerous.

....

Q3   Read Chapter Seven from "**Here, on the other side**" to "**mouth strained open.**" What does this description suggest about the island? Use a quote to support your answer.

....

....

....

Q4   How can you tell that Simon is more in harmony with nature than the other boys? Explain your answer.

....

....

Q5   In Chapter Eleven, the beach where Simon was killed has been "**swept clean**" and the sand is "**smooth again**". What does this suggest about nature? Explain your answer.

....

....

....

EXAM TIP

Shadows and Tall Trees — the roots of all evil...

If you're struggling to write about nature, look at how Golding describes the island at different points in the novel — changes in the island's atmosphere often reflect the plot, like at the end of Chapter Nine.

Section Three — Context and Themes

Games

Q1   Find a quote that suggests that the boys treat each of the following as a game.

    a) Collecting wood for the fire. (Chapter Two)

    ....

    b) Sitting in an assembly. (Chapter Five)

    ....

Q2   Read Chapter Three from "**Ralph surveyed the wreck**" to "**We want meat.**"
    What later event does the boys' attitude towards work foreshadow?

    ....

    ....

Q3   Golding gives the reader clues that the boys will become more violent by the end of
    the novel. Fill in the table to explain how each of the games below turns more violent.

Event	How the game turns more violent
a) The littluns build sand castles by the stream.	
b) Robert pretends to be a pig and the others chase him.	

Q4   In Chapter Twelve, the naval officer describes the boys' activities as "**Fun and games**". Do
    you think this is an accurate reflection of the boys' actions in the novel? Explain your answer.

    ....

    ....

    ....

Nowadays they'd all be too busy on their phones...

Explain how games are presented in the novel.
You should write about:
- how the games the characters play are presented in the novel
- how the characters' games change as the novel progresses.

Section Three — Context and Themes

Evil

Q1 Read Chapter Nine from **"His tone conveyed a warning"** to **"We shan't hear it."** How does Golding associate darkness with evil in this passage? Support your answer with an example.

....

....

....

....

© Alastair Muir/REX/Shutterstock

Q2 In Chapter Nine, all of the boys take part in the hunting dance that ends with Simon's murder. What do you think this suggests about evil in the novel? Explain your answer.

....

....

Q3 Read the following statements about Jack. Which one best represents how Jack's evil instincts are presented in the novel?

It is clear that Jack has evil instincts from the very beginning of the novel. ☐

Jack recognises that his actions are evil by the end of the novel. ☐

Jack's love of hunting and his desire for power lead him to commit evil acts. ☐

Q4 How does Golding use the scene with Simon and the Lord of the Flies in Chapter Eight to show the struggle between good and evil in the novel? Use a quote to support your answer.

....

....

....

Q5 Do you think the boys are saved from their own evil when the officer arrives? Explain your answer.

....

....

....

The Lord of the Flies seemed to bug Simon...

PRACTICE TASK

Make a list of three points in the novel when Ralph displays signs of evil — they could be things he does, says or thinks. For each point, write a brief explanation of how it links to the theme of evil.

 ☐   ☐ 😊 ☐

Writing about Context

To get a high mark in the exam, you need to write about the novel's context. *Lord of the Flies* was written in the 1950s, a few years after the end of World War Two, so you need to know about what Britain was like at the time, and which historical events may have influenced Golding. Adding contextual information and linking it to the key themes of the novel will help improve your answer. The questions on this page will get you thinking about context and how to use it in your responses.

Q1 Read the sample answer extracts below and underline the contextual information.

> **a)** Ralph and Jack have opposing leadership styles. Ralph leads by establishing rules that everyone must follow, arguing that they "are the only thing" the boys have left of civilisation. However, Jack rejects these rules and uses violence to force the others to obey him. Jack's abuse of power in the novel associates him with the dictator Adolf Hitler, who used threats of violence to ensure obedience before and during the Second World War. This contrast between Jack's dictatorial behaviour and Ralph's fairness emphasises their very different approaches to leadership. Throughout the novel, Golding uses this contrast to represent the ideological conflict between democracy and dictatorship in the 'adult' world beyond the island.

> **b)** Golding uses the choirboys to explore ideas about social class. The choirboys are presented as upper-class, as they wear uniforms that include "cloaks" and caps, and mention "matins", a religious service often held in public schools. In the 1950s, some people believed that boys who went to public school gained a greater sense of discipline, so Golding's use of clothing and language that are largely exclusive to those with a public school background signals to the reader that these boys should be self-disciplined. The fact that it is Jack, the leader of the choirboys, who encourages the choir to reject the rules and descend into savagery implies that Golding didn't believe in an automatic link between social class and self-discipline.

Q2 Write down a piece of context that could be included in the sample answer below.

> How does Golding present ideas about being British in *Lord of the Flies*?

> After finding the boys, the naval officer tells them that he thought a group of British boys would have "put up a better show". The way the naval officer unknowingly trivialises the boys' savagery highlights the contrast between his expectations and reality.

....

....

....

....

Practice Questions

Golding has rammed the book full of complex themes, so you need to make sure you've got your head around them all before your exam. The best way to do that is to practise, so we've got some more lovely questions for you to have a bash at. Plan your answers carefully and check through your work at the end.

Q1 Explain how fear is presented in *Lord of the Flies*.
You should write about:
- how fear is presented in the novel
- how fear is used to explore other ideas in the novel.

Q2 Golding wrote *Lord of the Flies* in the 1950s, shortly after the end of World War II.
In what ways is the novel's context significant?

Q3 Explain how nature is presented in *Lord of the Flies*.

Q4 Explore how Golding uses Ralph to present the theme of civilisation.
Make sure you refer to the novel's context in your answer.

Q5 **"authority sat on his shoulder and chattered in his ear like an ape."** (Chapter Nine)

How does Golding present power in the novel?
You should write about:
- how characters use their power
- why some characters don't have power.

Form in 'Lord of the Flies'

Q1 In a typical adventure story, the events take place in a remote location and the main characters have exciting adventures with no interference from adults. How does Golding use the events of Chapter One to suggest that *Lord of the Flies* will be like a typical adventure story?

....

....

....

Q2 Golding based *Lord of the Flies* on *The Coral Island* by R. M. Ballantyne, but he made some changes to the plot. Fill in the table to show how Golding's novel is different to Ballantyne's.

The Coral Island	Lord of the Flies
a) The boys get on well and support and remain loyal to each other throughout the novel.	The boys' loyalties become divided and they end up at war with one another.
b) The boys think they can hear ghosts, but they quickly realise the noises are just penguins.	
c) The boys intervene to stop savage acts such as cannibalism from being committed.	

Q3 How does the way that Golding adapts the plot of *The Coral Island* help him to convey his message about civilisation and barbarity?

....

....

Q4 *Lord of the Flies* could be read as an allegory for the collapse of democracy (a society where power is shared). What evidence is there in the novel to support this idea?

An allegory is a story where the characters and events can stand for something else.

....

....

....

The Coral Island vs. the quarrel island...

If you're writing about form, think about why Golding mirrors classic adventure novels. For example, giving the novel elements of a typical adventure makes the boys' actions seem even more shocking.

Structure and Viewpoint

Q1 In Chapter Two, the boys' fire gets out of hand and kills a littlun. What event does this foreshadow? Explain how Golding's use of foreshadowing affects the reader's response to the later event.

© Johan Persson/ArenaPAL

Event: ....

....

Explanation: ....

....

....

Q2 The novel's time scheme is very loose — Golding doesn't make it clear how long the boys spend on the island. Why do you think he does this?

....

....

Q3 At the start of the novel, Ralph is described as "**The boy with fair hair**" and Piggy is "**the fat boy**". Explain how this makes the narrator seem neutral.

....

....

Q4 Golding tells the story from the viewpoint of different characters. When Simon is killed, the story is from the perspective of the whole group. What effect does this have?

....

....

Q5 In Chapter Six, when Sam and Eric mistake the airman for the beast, the story switches from their perspective to Ralph's perspective. Why might Golding have chosen to do this?

....

....

....

MAKING LINKS

All these shifts in perspective are making me dizzy...

Golding uses repeated assemblies to show how conflict develops between the boys. You can make links between their behaviour at each assembly to show how the boys' conflict becomes more serious.

Section Four — The Writer's Techniques

Language — How the Characters Speak

Q1 Read Chapter One from **"Immured in these tangles"** to **"But they left at last."** How does the boys' language make them seem childlike? Support your answer with an example.

....

....

Q2 How does the choirboys' speech change as the novel progresses? Explain how this affects the reader's view of the choir.

....

....

....

Q3 Answer the following questions about Piggy's language.

a) How does Piggy's language differ from the way the other boys speak? Back up your answer with a quote.

....

....

b) Explain what this difference suggests about Piggy.

....

....

Q4 Read the start of Chapter Eleven, when Ralph's group holds an assembly. Find a quote from this assembly where Ralph's speech is hesitant. Explain how this makes him seem unsure.

Quote: ....

Explanation: ....

....

....

Wacco, Wizard, Whee-oh! — another task...

The littluns' speech tends to be simpler and more repetitive than that of the older boys. Write a few sentences explaining how Golding uses Phil's language in Chapter Five to make him seem young.

Language — The Writer's Effects

Q1   In Chapter Two, Jack says the boys need rules because they are "**not savages**".

Irony can occur when there is a difference between what the characters or the reader expects and what happens.

   a)   Explain how this creates irony later in the novel.

   ....

   ....

   b)   Give another example of irony in the novel.

   ....

   ....

Q2   Read Chapter Four from "**Ralph climbed out of the bathing-pool**" to "**— I apologise**". Answer the questions below.

   a)   Why does Golding uses Piggy's glasses to symbolise reason and logic?

   ....

   ....

   ....

   b)   Jack damages Piggy's glasses. What does this foreshadow?

© Columbia/courtesy Everett Collection Inc / Alamy Stock Photo

   ....

Q3   Read the description of the island at the start of Chapter Four. Explain how Golding uses language to make the island seem like a magical paradise. What effect does this have on the reader?

   Explanation: ....

   ....

   Effect: ....

   ....

Q4   At the start of the novel, Jack and his friends are called "**the choir**", but they are soon known as "**the hunters**". By the end of the text, they are "**savages**". What does this change suggest?

   ....

   ....

   ....

Q5 Find examples from Chapter Six of the language techniques
in the table below, then give the effect that each one has.

Technique	Example	Effect
Repetition	*"Down, down, the waters went"*	
Personification		
Simile		

Q6 Read Chapter Twelve from "**Ralph edged forward**" to "**Roger sharpened a stick at both ends.**"
How does Golding's language affect the pace of the novel? Support your answer with a quote.

....

....

....

Q7 After Simon dies in Chapter Nine, his cheek becomes
"**silvered**" and his shoulder turns into "**sculpted marble**".

a) Explain what impression of Simon this language gives the reader.

....

....

b) What effect does this imagery have on the reader?

....

....

Also by Golding — 101 Ways to Describe an Island...

Write an answer to the following question: **Explore how Golding creates a threatening atmosphere
in *Lord of the Flies*.** You should write about how he uses language and other techniques to create a
threatening atmosphere. Jot down a quick plan before you start, just like you would in the exam.

Close Language Analysis

Authors choose their language very carefully — every word in *Lord of the Flies* is there for a reason. Close language analysis is about really getting into the text and asking yourself exactly why a particular word is used and what effect it has on the reader. It may sound a bit tricky, but the questions on this page will give you some good practice of how to use close language analysis in your answers.

Q1 The bullet points below form part of a P.E.E.D. paragraph (see p.15). Read through the points and choose an appropriate piece of close language analysis from the numbered list which explains the example. Then write a short paragraph explaining your choice.

> - Piggy is presented as an isolated character.
> - In Chapter Four, when Piggy's glasses are taken from him, Golding describes him as being "islanded in a sea of meaningless colour".
> - Piggy is the most rational character in the novel, so taking away his ability to see and understand the world is a step towards the loss of rationality and logic on the island.

1) The word "sea" alludes to the fact that the boys are stuck in the middle of the ocean, suggesting that they are all able to sympathise with the way Piggy feels.

2) The word "islanded" gives the impression that, by taking Piggy's glasses, the other boys deliberately isolate him, leaving him feeling helpless and alone.

3) The word "meaningless" suggests that Piggy has become isolated because the other boys don't understand his sophisticated ideas.

Piece of close language analysis: ....

Explanation of choice: ....

....

....

Q2 In the sentences below, each quote contains one word that is underlined. For each underlined word, explain why you think Golding chose it. One has been done for you.

a) When Ralph runs up the mountain to relight the fire, he uses "**<u>precious</u> breath to swear**". The word "precious" emphasises how valuable Ralph's breath is; the fact that he wastes any breath to swear shows how angry he is that the fire has gone out.

b) When Ralph suggests that more than two of them should hunt the beast, all the boys leave and Roger is the only one who "**moved against the <u>tide</u>**".

....

....

c) After Piggy is killed, the tribe threatening Ralph "**<u>swarmed</u> across the neck**" of Castle Rock.

....

....

Section Four — The Writer's Techniques

Practice Questions

After trotting your way through the techniques pages, it's time to poke your nose into a few more practice questions. Include points about the different techniques Golding uses to see how well this section has sunk in. Remember to scribble a quick plan for each question before you start, just like you would in the exam.

Q1 **"'I got the conch,' said Piggy, in a hurt voice. 'I got a right to speak.'"** (Chapter Two)

How does Golding present Piggy as an outsider in the novel?

Q2 Explore how the atmosphere of *Lord of the Flies* changes throughout the novel.

Q3 Explain how Golding presents savage behaviour in the novel.

You should write about:
• how Golding presents savage behaviour
• how Golding uses savage behaviour to convey key ideas.

Q4 **"You could see a knee disturb the mould. Now the other. Two hands. A spear."** (Chapter Twelve)

Explore how Golding creates suspense in *Lord of the Flies*.

Q5 Write about the importance of structure in *Lord of the Flies*.

You should write about:
• how Golding structures the novel
• how he uses structure to explore key themes.

Section Five — Exam Buster

Understanding the Question

Underline key words in the question

Q1 Underline the most important words in the following questions.
The first one has been done for you.

a) <u>Explain</u> <u>how</u> Golding <u>presents</u> the theme of <u>evil</u> in the novel.

b) What is the significance of Simon in *Lord of the Flies*?

c) Explain how the theme of barbarity is explored in *Lord of the Flies*.

d) How does Golding create tension in *Lord of the Flies*?

e) Explain how the importance of good leadership is explored in the novel.

f) How is the character of Ralph presented in the novel?

g) Explain why the boys change in *Lord of the Flies*.

Make sure you understand exam language

Q2 Match each exam question to the correct explanation of what you would
need to do to answer it. You'll only need to use each white box once.

a) Explain how Golding presents the theme of evil in the novel.	**1)** Analyse how a character contributes to the action and overall message of the novel.
b) What is the significance of Simon in *Lord of the Flies*?	**2)** Analyse how Golding writes about a character.
c) Explain how the importance of good leadership is explored in the novel.	**3)** Analyse the reasons for a development or event in the text.
d) How is the character of Ralph presented in the novel?	**4)** Analyse how a theme contributes to the action and overall message of the novel.
e) Explain why the boys change in *Lord of the Flies*.	**5)** Analyse how Golding writes about a theme in the novel.

Exam language — mainly just sighs of despair...

No matter how keen you might be to start your essay, make sure you read the question several times and think
about exactly what you're being asked to do. You don't want to end up writing about the wrong thing...

Making a Rough Plan

Jot down your main ideas

Q1 Look at the exam question below, then complete the spider diagram with at least three more main points for answering it.

Don't forget to underline the key words in the question before you start.

He helps Golding to explore ideas about barbarity.

How is the character of Jack significant in *Lord of the Flies*?

Put your best points and examples in a logical order

Q2 Choose your three best points from Q1 and fill in the plan below, adding evidence (a quote or an example from the novel) for each point.

(Introduction)

Point One: ....

Evidence: ....

Point Two: ....

Evidence: ....

Point Three: ....

Evidence: ....

(Conclusion)

Don't jump to conclusions — plan your essay carefully...

A plan is your friend. It'll help you stay focused under pressure, stop you going off track and reassure you if you start to panic. And it only takes five minutes of your time — I'm sure you can spare that for such a good friend...

Section Five — Exam Buster

Making Links

Make links with other parts of the text

Q1 Look at the exam question and the table below. Complete the table with other relevant parts of the text which could be used to back up each point.

> Write about how Golding presents violence in *Lord of the Flies*.

Point	Example 1	Example 2
Violence is a feature of Jack's leadership.	Jack violently punishes the boys in his tribe.	
Violence increases as the novel progresses.	The hunting dances get more violent and lead to Simon's death.	
Violence exists in the outside world as well as on the island.	The dead airman shows that there's a war going on.	

Extend your essay with other examples

You won't have time to do really detailed planning in the exam so you should get into the habit of quickly thinking of links when you're doing practice questions.

Q2 Look back at the points you included in your plan in Q2 on p.43. For each point, write down another example from a different part of the text that you could include in your essay.

Example for Point One: ....

....

Example for Point Two: ....

....

Example for Point Three: ....

....

If you liked this page, you may also like page 23...

Finding links between different parts of the text will make your answer more convincing and show that you have a solid understanding of the novel. It's a lot easier to do this if you're really familiar with the text, so get reading...

Structuring Your Answer

P.E.E.D. stands for Point, Example, Explain, Develop

Q1 Read the following extract from an exam answer. Label each aspect of P.E.E.D.

> Golding uses the boys' appearance to show that they become more savage as the novel progresses. When Jack is first introduced, he is wearing a school uniform, but he quickly begins to hunt wearing only "tattered shorts". Jack's uniform represents the discipline of his previous life, so the fact that it gets torn suggests that his civilised values are fading. The idea that the boys' appearance reflects their increasing barbarity is echoed when Jack begins to paint his face, which provides a "liberation into savagery".

Embedding quotes is a great way to give evidence

Q2 Rewrite the following sentences so that a short part of the quote is embedded in each one.

    a) The Lord of the Flies tells Simon that evil is inside him — "I'm part of you".

    ....

    b) Piggy claims that Simon's death wasn't really murder — "It was an accident".

    ....

Structure your answer using the P.E.E.D. method

Q3 Use the P.E.E.D. method to structure a paragraph on your first point from Q2 on page 43.

Point: ....

....

Example: ....

....

Explain: ....

....

Develop: ....

....

Surely you didn't think I'd stoop that low...

This is a serious and important topic in a serious and important publication — it's no place for toilet humour. (Tee hee.) Using the P.E.E.D. method will make sure your paragraphs are beautifully clear and structured.

Introductions and Conclusions

Give a clear answer to the question in your introduction

Q1 Read the question and the introduction extracts below. Decide which is better and explain why.

> Explain how Piggy is presented as an intelligent character in *Lord of the Flies*.

a)
> Piggy is a very important character in *Lord of the Flies*. His intelligence is shown many times in the novel, for example when he suggests that the group make sundials so they can tell the time. In addition, he shows loyalty to Ralph and doesn't lose faith in him as a leader. He also understands what's going on more than some of the other boys.

b)
> Golding presents Piggy as an intelligent character in various ways. Piggy's insights into other characters show that he is perceptive and is able to think deeply. His logic and rational thinking also make it easier for the boys to survive on the island. However, Piggy's intelligence isn't always presented positively; at times, it blinds him to the threat of the boys' savage behaviour.

Better intro: .... Reason: ....

....

....

....

Don't write any new points in your conclusion

Q2 Read the conclusion to the exam question in Q1, then say how it could be improved.

> To summarise, Piggy is presented as a civilised character. He behaves maturely and thinks carefully about what's happening. Another important time when Piggy shows intelligence is when he warns Ralph that "There's going to be trouble" on the night of Simon's death. This shows that he is perceptive.

....

....

....

....

....

I find introductions tricky — I'm terrible with names...

Have a go at writing an introduction and a conclusion for the exam question on p.43. Keep in mind the good and bad examples you've looked at on this page and make sure what you write is relevant to your main points.

Writing about Context

Make sure you can link the novel to its context

Q1 Match each event with the relevant contextual information.

a) Roger carries out violent acts, such as torturing Sam and Eric to make them join Jack's tribe.

1) Children who attended elite public schools were used to a strict hierarchy.

b) Jack believes that his status as head boy and chapter chorister means that he should be the boys' chief.

2) Himmler, an important figure in Hitler's Nazi party, committed terrible crimes against groups such as Jews.

c) The boys struggle to perform all the tasks they want to once they have split into smaller groups.

3) By the 1950s, the British Empire was weaker than it had been previously because it had lost many colonies.

Include context in your answer

Q2 Read the sample answer below and underline the contextual information. Then write a paragraph using your second point from page 43 and include contextual information of your own. Use the P.E.E.D. method.

> Golding suggests that the world beyond the island is being destroyed by war. In Chapter One, Piggy challenges Ralph's assumption that his father will come to their rescue by repeating "They're all dead." The repetition of the word "all" emphasises the widespread devastation caused by the atom bomb. The idea that a nuclear attack would have terrible consequences reflects the fear of conflict breaking out between the USA and the USSR during the Cold War; both countries had nuclear weapons which had the potential to cause large-scale destruction.

....

....

....

....

....

....

I sent my mate a joke message — he really fell for my con-text...

You'll impress the examiner if you can make links between events in the novel and its context. One way you could do this is by writing about how the social expectations of the time influence the characters' behaviour.

Linking Ideas and Paragraphs

Link your ideas so your argument is easy to follow

Q1 Rewrite the sample answer below, adding words and/or phrases so the ideas are clearly linked.

> The other boys treat Piggy unkindly. In Chapter One, Ralph doesn't apologise for revealing Piggy's nickname to the others at first. Ralph says "Better Piggy than Fatty". He doesn't respect Piggy. Golding shows that people with a privileged background are not necessarily always kind or moral.

....

....

....

....

....

Q2 Write a paragraph using your third point from p.43. Make sure your ideas are properly connected.

....

....

....

....

....

Show how your paragraphs follow on from each other

Q3 Look at the three paragraphs you have written on pages 45, 47 and in Q2 on this page. Write down linking words or phrases you could use to link them together in your answer.

Paragraphs to link	Linking word or phrase
p.45 and p.47	
p.47 and p.48	

Click on this <u>link</u> for guaranteed exam success...*

No one is trying to catch you out in the exam, so don't panic. Make sure you read the question carefully and please, *please* spend five minutes planning — it'll help you no end.

*Easy way out currently unavailable due to technical problems

Marking Answer Extracts

Get familiar with the mark scheme

Grade band	An answer at this level...
8-9	• shows an insightful and critical personal response to the text • closely and perceptively analyses how the writer uses language, form and structure to create meaning and affect the reader, making use of highly relevant subject terminology • supports arguments with well-integrated, highly relevant and precise examples from the text • gives a detailed exploration of the relationship between the text and its context • uses highly varied vocabulary and sentence types, with mostly accurate spelling and punctuation
6-7	• shows a critical and observant personal response to the text • includes a thorough exploration of how the writer uses language, form and structure to create meaning and affect the reader, making use of appropriate subject terminology • supports arguments with integrated, well-chosen examples from the text • explores the relationship between the text and its context • uses a substantial range of vocabulary and sentence types, with generally accurate spelling and punctuation
4-5	• shows a thoughtful and clear personal response to the text • examines how the writer uses language, form and structure to create meaning and affect the reader, making some use of relevant subject terminology • integrates appropriate examples from the text • shows an understanding of contextual factors • uses a moderate range of vocabulary and sentence types, without spelling and punctuation errors which make the meaning unclear

Have a go at marking an answer extract

Q1 Using the mark scheme, put the sample answer extract below in a grade band and explain why.

> Explain the significance of the boys' games in *Lord of the Flies*.

> Golding uses the game where Roger threw stones at Henry in Chapter Four to show that the boys are still following the rules of civillisation. Roger throws "to miss" Henry because of the "taboo of the old life". This suggests that he wants to hit Henry but doesn't do so because he knows its not socially acceptable, since public schoolboys in the 1950s had to obey rules. Later in the novel, Roger murders Piggy almost as part of a game, which emphasises that he is no longer civilised.

Grade band: .... Reason: ....

....

....

....

Marking Answer Extracts

Have a look at these extracts from answers to the question on page 49

Q1 For each extract, say what grade band you think it is in, then underline an example of where it meets each of the mark scheme criteria. Label each underlined point to show what it achieves.

---

a) Golding uses the recurring game in which the boys re-enact a hunt to show their increasing savagery, through the intensification of Ralph's violent instincts. In Chapter Four, Ralph feels "envious" while watching the others 'hunt' Maurice in such a game, but he does not participate. However, in a similar game in Chapter Seven, Ralph's urge to "squeeze and hurt" Robert is "over-mastering". The word "over-mastering" creates the impression that Ralph's mind has been overpowered by his brutal impulses, suggesting that he is no longer able to suppress his impulse to hurt others. The fact that Ralph, who generally represents civilised values, is unable to resist his violent urges reinforces Golding's message that everyone has a savage side.

Golding also uses games to hint that Ralph is in a vulnerable position as leader. In Chapter Seven, the narrator states that Ralph makes decisions as though he is "playing chess". Chess is a battle of minds between two opponents, where one wrong move can result in a player losing their power. Comparing Ralph's decisions to chess moves highlights that he might make a mistake at any time that will enable Jack, his opponent, to defeat him. The boys' situation could be viewed as an allegory for the Cold War, when the threat of nuclear war was imminent. Jack and Ralph represent the world leaders of the time, who could have triggered a catastrophic war with one misjudged action or decision. In this way, the devastating fire in the final chapter could be viewed as a warning to those in power.

Grade band: ....

---

b) Golding uses games to emphasise the boys' youth and innocence. In Chapter Six, Jack and his tribe think that Castle Rock would make a "wizard fort". The adjective "wizard" is a slang word that was often used by public schoolboys in the 1950s. Its use here highlights the boys' childish excitement, while the way they imagine the rock to be a "fort" emphasises their innocence, as it shows that they are treating life on the island as a game. Later in the novel, Ralph's realisation that calling "pax", a truce used by schoolchildren in the mid-20th century, won't protect him from Jack shows that the boys' conflict is not a game, which shows that their innocence has been lost.

The boys use games as a way of coping with the dangers of life on the island. In Chapter Seven, some of the boys tread along a difficult path "as if they were climbing a dangerous mountain". By imagining the path to be part of a "dangerous mountain", the boys put their situation into the context of a game in which they are going on an exciting adventure. This helps them to make the danger that they are facing seem less threatening. However, there are constant reminders for the reader that the boys' situation is genuinely dangerous, such as Robert cutting his leg "quite badly". These reminders contribute to the tense atmosphere of the novel because they show that the boys' adventurous games are likely to result in some of the boys being seriously hurt.

Grade band: ....

Marking a Whole Answer

Now try marking this whole answer

Q1 Read the sample answer below. On page 52, put it in a grade band and explain your decision.

> How is the conflict between civilisation and barbarity presented in *Lord of the Flies*?

If it helps you, label examples of where the answer meets the mark scheme criteria.

In *Lord of the Flies*, Golding presents the conflict between civilisation and barbarity as an ongoing confrontation within every person. He develops this idea by presenting civilised values and barbaric impulses as opposing forces through symbolism and through the characters of Ralph and Jack. In addition, he presents the struggle between civilisation and barbarity as damaging by emphasising its divisive nature and underlining the destructive consequences that barbarity can have on civilised society. Finally, Golding uses characters' appearances to imply that neither barbarity nor civilisation can ever be fully erased from a person's nature.

Golding adapts the adventure story form to present the conflict between barbarity and civilisation as a struggle that exists within every individual. In traditional British adventure stories, 'civilised' British characters often come into conflict with primitive, fierce 'savages' from remote places. However, in *Lord of the Flies*, British public schoolboys who have had privileged upbringings gradually become 'savages' themselves. This deviation from the adventure story form allows Golding to present the conflict between civilisation and barbarity as an internal one faced by every person, even if they come from a 'civilised' society. Golding uses this adaptation of form to challenge a belief held by many British people in the 1950s that they were superior to those from supposedly less-civilised countries in the British Empire.

Golding uses symbolism to develop his presentation of the conflict between civilisation and barbarity within a person. Throughout the novel, hunting is used to reinforce the boys' lust for violence and the pleasure they take in inflicting pain, so it acts as a symbol of barbarity. Conversely, the signal fire symbolises civilisation, as the boys cannot hope to be rescued and return to civilised society without it. The fact that, in Chapter Four, Jack's hunters would rather hunt than take care of the fire hints that their barbaric instincts have a stronger influence on them than their desire to be part of a civilised society. In Chapter Eight, after Jack leaves to start his own tribe, the logs for Ralph's signal fire crumble into a "sodden" mess, which gives the impression that they are decaying and useless. The disintegration of the wood symbolises the deterioration of the boys' chances of returning to civilisation as more of them resort to savagery.

One of the characters in whom this struggle between civilisation and barbarity is clearest is Ralph; Golding uses shifts in narrative perspective to give insights into Ralph's internal conflict. In Chapter Five, the focus shifts from an argument between the group to Ralph's recognition that the others don't recognise the signal fire as "all-important". In Chapter Ten, Golding uses a similar shift from an argument between Ralph and the twins to Ralph's bewildered attempt to remember why the fire is important. By creating a direct comparison between Ralph's thoughts at different points in the novel, Golding makes it clear to the reader that Ralph is losing his grasp on why civilised values, represented by the fire, are important. This suggests that the power of civilisation on the island is weakening as the power of barbarity increases. However, the fact that, even in his state of confusion, Ralph views the signal fire as "overwhelmingly good" suggests that he is instinctively drawn to civilisation, hinting that its power is not entirely lost.

This answer continues on p.52. ⟶

Marking a Whole Answer

Golding also uses the character of Ralph to present the conflict between civilisation and barbarity as divisive, through his relationship with Jack. In Chapter Four, after their confrontation about whether to prioritise the signal fire or hunting, Ralph and Jack end up on "different sides" of a "high barrier" created by the new signal fire. This physical separation reflects the ideological division between Ralph, who favours civilised values, and Jack, who represents barbaric impulses, showing that civilisation and barbarity are opposing forces. This physical and metaphorical barrier between Ralph and Jack foreshadows the way in which the boys' society on the island splits into two distinct groups later in the novel due to their opposing views on the value of civilisation.

As well as using the symbols of fire and hunting to reflect the internal conflict between civilisation and barbarity within everyone, Golding also uses symbolism to demonstrate the destructive impact that barbarity can have on civilisation. In Chapter Four, the littluns' sand castle "complex", which resembles a developed civilisation, is quickly destroyed by Roger and Maurice, who scatter its "chosen stones". The adjective "chosen" gives the impression that the complex has been thoughtfully constructed. The fact that these stones are easily displaced by Roger and Maurice's violence therefore implies that a single barbaric act can quickly destroy a well-crafted civilisation. This could be an allusion to the widespread destruction caused by bombing raids during World War Two, in which large areas of towns and cities could be devastated in seconds, reinforcing Golding's message that even the most established societies are vulnerable to barbarity.

Golding also suggests that it is not always clear when barbarity has prevailed. In Chapter Twelve, he presents the naval officer's civilised appearance as a disguise that hides his barbarity. The officer wears a neat "white" uniform and arrives on a "trim cruiser". The colour white often symbolises peace and purity, which suggests that the officer is moral, while the adjective "trim" indicates that the ship is smart and unblemished. The officer's respectable appearance masks the fact that he is actually part of a war that is destroying civilisation. Golding hints that the reverse is also true and that civilisation can be hidden behind a savage exterior; in the final chapter, the "small savages" become "little boys" again when they are rescued, hinting that remnants of their civilised values still exist.

Golding's presentation of the conflict between civilisation and barbarity is mainly pessimistic. He presents this conflict as both inescapable and enduring through his depiction of the ongoing, internal struggle that all people face between abiding by civilised values and following their barbaric instincts. The presentation of the destructive effects of barbarity on civilisation and Ralph's gradual loss of his own sense of civilisation ultimately suggest that barbarity is more powerful than civilisation. However, Golding offers the reader a glimmer of hope in the final chapter, when he hints that the boys' connection to civilisation has not been entirely severed.

Grade band: .... Reasons: ....

....

....

....

....

Mark schemes — he's always got a cunning plan...

If you're really familiar with the mark scheme for your exam board, you'll know exactly what the examiner is looking for. You're being tested on several skills, so you'll need to demonstrate all of them to get a top mark.

Writing Well

Spelling, punctuation and grammar (SPaG for short) might not be the most exciting things in the world, but in the exam marks will be awarded for good English, so you don't want to miss out. Using a variety of sentence structures and vocabulary will also make your answer more impressive. It's a good idea to leave a few minutes at the end of the exam to check through your work for silly mistakes, like misspelt names. On this page you'll have the chance to hone your skills.

Q1 Read the sample answer below. Underline the SPaG mistakes, then correct them. One has already been done for you.

> *symbol*
> The conch is a <u>cymbal</u> which represents civilisation. It is initally a practical tool that is used
>
> to call meetings and indicate when a boy is allowed to speak, with all of the boys respecting
>
> it's status. However, as the novel progresses, the power of the conch begins to dissappear as
>
> the boys barbaric instincts take over from there regard for the rules on the island. Eventually,
>
> the conch is smashed into a "thousand white fragments", reflecting Jack's tribe's complete
>
> abandonment of civilisation when they intentionly murder Piggy.

Q2 Rewrite the following sentences, using appropriate language for the exam.

a) Piggy has glasses so he seems loads cleverer than the other kids.

....

....

b) The weather makes the dance bit where Simon is killed scarier.

....

....

c) Simon seems like a bit of a loner.

....

....

d) The littluns whinge a lot and won't shut up about the beast.

....

....

Practice Questions

Now you've polished your essay-writing skills, have a bash at doing these practice questions under exam conditions. Spend five minutes doing a rough plan and about 40 minutes writing your essay. Use the techniques you've learnt in this section and leave a bit of time to check through your answer at the end.

Q1 How is Simon used to present ideas about good and evil in *Lord of the Flies*?

Q2 Explain how civilised values are significant in *Lord of the Flies*.

You should write about:
- times when characters show civilised values
- how civilised values are used to explore ideas about society.

Q3 How does Golding use the characters and events of *Lord of the Flies* to explore its context?

Q4 **"The thing is — fear can't hurt you any more than a dream."** (Jack, Chapter Five)

Explain how fear is significant in *Lord of the Flies*.

Q5 How is Piggy presented as a good friend in the novel?

You should write about:
- times when Piggy shows that he is a good friend
- how Golding uses Piggy's treatment of others to convey ideas to the reader.

Answers

Section One — Analysis of Chapters

Page 2: Chapter One — The Sound of the Shell

1. E.g. The palm trees and "dazzling beach" make it seem like a tropical paradise. However, there are references to things like "skull-like" coconuts, which hint that it might be dangerous.
2. a) False: e.g. "Sucks to your auntie!"
   b) True: e.g. "We may stay here till we die."
   c) True: e.g. "Choir! Stand still!"
3. E.g. Yes, because their democratic vote shows that civilised values such as fairness are important to them. Jack behaves in a civilised way by not contesting the outcome. **Or** e.g. No, because Ralph isn't chosen based on his skill or intelligence, but because he is the one who blows the conch. This makes the boys seem uncivilised.
4. He is disgusted by the idea of killing it — he feels that its blood would be "unbearable" and he struggles with having to cut into "living flesh". / Killing the piglet would be an "enormity", which implies that he is still controlled by the rules of civilised society.
Task: Here are some points you may have included if you chose Ralph:
   - He is keen to appoint a chief, which suggests that he recognises the importance of having a strong leader.
   - He is talented — he is a good swimmer and learns how to blow the conch quickly. This makes him seem bright and competent, which might make him a good leader.
   - He is the one who blows the conch and summons the other boys. He therefore seems to be the only one doing anything constructive.
   Here are some points you may have included if you chose Jack:
   - He leads the choir from where they landed to the platform, which shows that he is a natural leader.
   - He is head boy and chapter chorister, which means that he has experience in leadership positions.
   - His voice shows that he "knew his own mind". This suggests that he is decisive and will get things done.

Page 3: Chapter Two — Fire on the Mountain

1. The statements should be numbered 4, 3, 6, 1, 5, 2.
2. He knows that the beast is not real, but his attempt to explain why it can't exist has no effect on the littluns, who remain scared.
3. a) E.g. He is ashamed. "The shameful knowledge grew in them"
   b) E.g. He thinks that they should all follow the rule. "I got the conch! Just you listen!"
4. E.g. The way that a tree explodes "like a bomb" suggests that the fire can kill people. The fact that the fire has spread to the trees implies that it would be difficult to escape from.
Task: Here are some points you may have included:
   - The tension created by the conflict between Ralph and Jack in Chapter One is heightened in Chapter Two. Whereas Ralph claims that the beast doesn't exist, Jack promises to look for it. This makes Ralph feel "defeated", suggesting that his position as chief is threatened.
   - The littluns' fear of the beast makes Chapter Two more tense. Even though the older boys claim that the beast isn't real, the idea that the island they thought was "uninhabited" might be home to a beast creates a sense of danger.
   - The apparent death of the boy with the mulberry birthmark creates a tense atmosphere. In Chapter One the boys thought they were going to have fun on the island. The death of the littlun makes the other boys look "fearfully" at one another as it becomes clear that their 'games' may have serious consequences.

Page 4: Chapter Three — Huts on the Beach

1. E.g. It seems overgrown and claustrophobic. It could be easy to get lost in, as Jack sees "only the faintest indication of a trail".
2. a) E.g. "Never get it done."
   b) E.g. "Only I know how they feel."

3. E.g. It suggests that they are aware of the differences between them and are confused by their feelings towards one another. On the one hand, they respect one another, but on the other, they know that they are rivals.
4. Simon, surrounded, isolates, different, magical
Task: Here are some points you may have included:
   - Ralph and Simon are builders. Piggy and the littluns are supposed to be building shelters too, but don't help much. Ralph wants the shelters to protect the boys from the weather and make them feel safe, which shows that he wants to look after the whole group. The fact that he wants to make the island more like home suggests that he values civilisation.
   - Jack and some of the older boys are hunters. They believe that the boys need meat, and they want to spend all their time hunting. The fact that they choose hunting over building suggests that they are adventurous, but also hints that they are selfish because they could do both. Golding also presents them as barbaric through the way they seem to enjoy the idea of hurting animals.

Page 5: Chapter Four — Painted Faces and Long Hair

1. false, true, false, true
2. E.g. He may have wanted to hint that some of the boys have a desire to hurt one another. This makes it more likely that they will commit evil acts later in the novel.
3. E.g. He becomes more savage — his laughter becomes a "bloodthirsty snarling". He also starts to dance, which reflects the idea that he is now "liberated from shame".
4. a) E.g. "They let the bloody fire out."
   b) E.g. "You and your hunting!"
   c) E.g. "That was a dirty trick."

Page 6: Chapter Five — Beast from Water

1. E.g. Ralph admires Piggy for his ability to think logically, but the fact that he refers to Piggy's "ludicrous" body suggests that his view of him is not entirely positive.
2. E.g. The boys' fear makes them unable to think rationally. / Jack's promise to hunt the beast makes them feel as though there is something to be afraid of.
3. a) Piggy, e.g. It shows he's ashamed of how the boys are acting.
   b) Ralph, e.g. It shows he's lost confidence in himself.
4. E.g. The boys don't take what Ralph says as seriously as before, and Jack shows his disregard for Ralph's leadership by exclaiming "Bollocks to the rules!"
Task: Here are some points you may have included:
   - It was a good idea to build a fire on the mountain like the boys did, but they could have organised it better so that the fire didn't get out of hand.
   - It may have been better to build the shelters earlier and ensure that all of the boys took part in building them.
   - The boys could have set aside a particular time for hunting so that the hunters still got to hunt but weren't distracted from more important tasks like building huts.

Page 7: Chapter Six — Beast from Air

1. E.g. By revealing to the reader that the "beast" Sam and Eric encounter later isn't real, he shows how powerful and misplaced the boys' fear is.
2. a) E.g. He's scared and wants to hide from it. "Couldn't we — kind of — stay here?"
   b) E.g. He wants to consider how best to tackle the beast. "So we've got to think."
   c) E.g. He has doubts about whether the beast is real. He "felt a flicker of incredulity".
3. E.g. He's dreading having to take the lead in approaching the beast. The fact that "the chief would have to go forward" is part of his "personal hell".
4. The ocean around Castle Rock is personified as a "stupendous creature", which makes it seem threatening. The rocks "totter", giving the impression that Castle Rock is unstable. There isn't much fresh water, which hints that people can't survive there.

Answers

Page 8: Chapter Seven — Shadows and Tall Trees

1. The statements should be numbered 2, 1, 4, 6, 5, 3.
2. E.g. Jack distracts the boys from Ralph's achievement by showing them his wound. He is jealous of the attention Ralph is getting and wants to remind the boys that he's a good hunter.
3. E.g. The rivalry between them means that neither Jack nor Ralph wants to back down. Jack's invitation is a "taunt" to provoke Ralph, so Ralph has to accept it to keep the respect of the group.
4. In Chapter One, the island is mainly described as a sunny paradise, whereas in this chapter, the island seems more threatening, with the boys caught between the "impassable" rocks by the sea and the "dark tunnel" of the forest.

Task: Here are some points you may have included:
- The littluns have been treated poorly as the older boys didn't prioritise doing things which could have made them feel safer (like building shelters). Some boys, like Jack and Maurice, allow them to go on being afraid of the beast. They are also bullied by older boys like Roger.
- Some of the older boys do try to help them. During the meeting in Chapter Two, Piggy helps the littlun speak by kneeling next to him with the conch, "listening and interpreting" for the rest of the group. Simon also helps them by finding them ripe fruit to eat.

Page 9: Chapter Eight — Gift for the Darkness

1. E.g. He claims that Ralph thinks the hunters are "no good". He knows that this will offend the hunters and make them see Ralph as a poor leader who doesn't appreciate them. / He suggests that Ralph is like Piggy (a figure the group doesn't respect) and he makes Ralph seem unreliable by saying that his actions on the mountain show that he's a "coward".
2. a) False: e.g. "We can do without Jack Merridew."
   b) False: e.g. "they worked with passion"
   c) True: e.g. "I seen them stealing off"
3. E.g. They think that the beast might come for the pig's head and are afraid of encountering it.
4. E.g. The pig's head tells Simon "I'm part of you". This implies that everyone has an evil side to them, as the 'beast' is even inside Simon, who is a very pure character.

Task: You should have written one paragraph from Jack's point of view, and one paragraph from Ralph's point of view. Here are some points you may have included:
- Jack — When he loses the vote, he is embarrassed, but when members of the group join him, he cheers up and looks "brilliantly happy".
- Ralph — Just after the split, he hopes that Jack will return. He loses the motivation to do things, but seems pleased when Piggy suggests building a new fire on the beach. He seems disappointed to find that so many of the other boys have joined Jack's tribe.

Page 10: Chapter Nine — A View to a Death

1. E.g. After clouds appear in the sky, the weather gets steadily worse, which creates a foreboding atmosphere. The thunderstorm during Simon's murder emphasises the violent circumstances of his death.
2. a) E.g. "The beast was harmless"
   b) E.g. "sat there like an idol"
   c) E.g. "They took the gift, dribbling."
3. E.g. He suggests that Jack's power comes from his physical strength.
4. E.g. The repetition of the chant reinforces the idea that the tribe is acting as a "single organism", rather than as individuals with a conscience. He also uses violent verbs, such as "screamed, struck, bit, tore", to make their actions seem barbaric.

Task: Here are some points you may have included:
- The weather becomes calmer, which hints to the reader that the danger has passed for now. Golding may have wanted to relieve the tension, allowing the reader to reflect on what has happened.

- Golding uses long descriptions of nature to slow down the pace at the end of the chapter. This creates a mournful mood and encourages the reader to think of Simon as a character whose death will be a big loss to the boys.
- At the end of the chapter, Golding emphasises the quietness of the setting; even the sound of the water fades away. This creates a contrast with the noisy, chaotic atmosphere during Simon's murder, emphasising the brutality of the boys' actions.

Page 11: Chapter Ten — The Shell and the Glasses

1. false, true, false, false
2. a) E.g. Robert seems to admire Jack. He agrees when Roger calls Jack a "proper Chief" and laughs "excitedly" at the idea of Wilfred being beaten.
   b) E.g. Earlier, he used the boys' fear of the beast to gain power, so he may be worried that if the boys feel more secure, he will lose influence.
3. E.g. The conch is a symbol of power, so having it would give the impression that Jack is the legitimate leader of the boys.
4. E.g. He has stolen Piggy's glasses, so he can now provide fire for the boys. This gives him more power.

Page 12: Chapter Eleven — Castle Rock

1. E.g. Sam and Eric seem keen to paint their faces in order to put them on a more equal footing with the tribe, but Ralph wants them to go as they are to show that they're not savages.
2. a) False: e.g. "The tribe of painted savages giggled"
   b) False: e.g. "Call that a signal fire?"
   c) True: e.g. "I got the conch!"
3. E.g. Piggy is defenceless against the giant boulder, which makes the tribe seem brutal and cowardly. / Piggy is killed just as he is making a passionate speech in favour of civilised values, which makes the tribe's actions seem particularly barbaric to the reader.
4. E.g. "That's what you'll get!"
   Any valid explanation, e.g. It shows that Jack wants to kill Ralph in the same way that Piggy was killed by the boulder.

Task: E.g. I would set the film in Antarctica. A team of explorers could get lost in a blizzard. Even though they would be adults and might therefore act more maturely than the characters in the novel, there may still be disagreements about how to be rescued. Fire, the boys' best hope of being rescued, might be replaced with a radio transmitter or a GPS tracker. Piggy's glasses, which enable the fire to be lit, could become batteries.

Page 13: Chapter Twelve — Cry of the Hunters

1. The statements should be numbered 4, 5, 2, 6, 3, 1.
2. E.g. By linking back to the earlier chapter, Golding implies that the tribe might treat Ralph in the same way that the pig in Chapter Eight was treated, creating a horrific and terrifying image.
3. E.g. Ralph wonders whether a fire could "outrun a galloping horse". Any valid explanation, e.g. By making it seem as though Ralph might die, Golding builds suspense and makes the arrival of the officer surprising.
4. E.g. He is moved because Ralph and the younger boys start to cry noisily. He may be embarrassed because men and boys were not supposed to show weakness at the time.

Task: Here are some events you may have included:
- The vote in Chapter One in which Ralph is elected chief
- Jack's apology to Ralph in Chapter Four
- The attempt to find the beast in Chapter Seven
- Jack's theft of Piggy's glasses in Chapter Ten
- The murder of Piggy by Jack's tribe in Chapter Eleven

In your summary of how the relationship between Ralph and Jack changes, you may have included the following points:
- Jack's treatment of Ralph becomes more violent during the course of the novel, particularly after Piggy's death.
- Initially, they are able to resolve the problems in their relationship, whereas later on, their problems become too serious to overcome.
- At the very end of the novel, Jack doesn't object when Ralph says that he's the boys' leader. This could suggest that he no longer wants to challenge Ralph and wants the conflict to end.

Answers

Page 14: Skills Focus — Using Quotes

1. accurate, relevant, irrelevant, embedded, important, repeat
   (Other answers are also possible.)
2. Good quote usage: a) and c) *[relevant and well embedded]*
   Bad quote usage: b) *[not embedded, irrelevant]*, d) *[not embedded]* and e) *[repeats point above too closely]*
3. You could have rewritten the examples as follows:
   b) Simon is presented as a kind and generous person, who provides the littluns with "double handfuls" of fruit.
   d) Simon believes that the beast isn't real, and that it's "only" them.
   e) In Chapter Four, the boys' laughter at Piggy becomes a "gale of hysteria".

Page 15: Skills Focus — P.E.E.D.

1. a) The Explain stage is missing. A sentence should be added to explain the quote, for example:
   Jack's use of insulting language shows that he is insensitive because he does not care about how others feel.
   b) The Example stage is missing. A specific example or a quote should be added to back up the initial statement, for example:
   Simon often chooses to spend time away from the other boys in his "place in the jungle".
   c) The Develop stage is missing. The answer should be extended by explaining the effect on the reader or linking the example to another aspect of the text, for example:
   Golding therefore reminds the reader that the barbarity that takes place during the novel is not confined to the island, as the outside world is also at war.

Section Two — Characters

Page 16: Ralph

1. a) E.g. "All day I've been working with Simon."
   b) E.g. "I'm chief. I'll go."
2. b) E.g. He is excited by violence.
   c) E.g. He can't believe how barbaric the other boys have become.
3. E.g. It suggests that he is ashamed of himself as he has realised how savage he must appear to the 'civilised' naval officer.
4. E.g. Ralph is partly responsible, as his conflict with Jack forces the group apart. This might have been avoided if Ralph had shared more of his power with Jack, as it could have stopped Jack from trying to take power by force. / Ralph does everything he can to create a stable society, but the other boys' reluctance to build shelters and maintain the signal fire undermines his efforts, meaning that they are more responsible for the breaking down of their society than he is.

Exam Practice:
Your answer should have an introduction, several paragraphs developing different ideas and a conclusion. You may have covered some of the following points:
* Golding presents Ralph's leadership as instinctive. In Chapter Six, something "deep in Ralph spoke for him" when he tells the others that he will face the beast. The fact that Ralph's compulsion to act on behalf of the others comes from "deep" within him emphasises that self-sacrifice is a fundamental part of his nature, which increases the impression that he is naturally suited to being a leader. This sense of natural leadership is evident from the start of the novel; in the first chapter, Golding describes Ralph as a "being" who is "set apart" from the other boys. The word "being" makes Ralph appear more than human, hinting that he is naturally superior to the other boys.
* Golding presents Ralph as a good leader through his bravery. In Chapter Eleven, when Ralph, Piggy and the twins go to confront Jack's tribe, they stop "with one accord" upon seeing Castle Rock, implying that they are equally paralysed by fear. Soon after this, Ralph challenges this fear by asking "What are we hiding for?" By verbalising this question, Ralph sets an example that encourages the others to overcome their own fear. This makes him seem like a good leader as it shows that he seeks to guide and nurture his followers by sharing his emotional strength with them.

* Ralph is presented as a good leader through the way he rules democratically. Just after being elected in the first assembly, Ralph puts Jack in charge of the choir, saying "They can be — what do you want them to be?" The way that Ralph's dialogue suddenly changes from a command to a question highlights that he is making a conscious effort not to dictate to Jack and to make him feel that his opinions are valued. Ralph's democratic rule would have seemed praiseworthy to British readers in the 1950s as there was great rivalry between the undemocratic USSR and democratic countries like the USA and Britain at this time.

Page 17: Piggy

1. E.g. Example: In Chapter Two, he says they should have built shelters first rather than going off to make a fire.
   Explanation: Piggy's behaviour annoys others, meaning that they take less notice of him. This makes him an outsider to the group.
2. E.g. He is the character with the strongest link to civilisation, as he remembers the importance of being rescued. His urgent tone suggests that he is desperate to make sure this link isn't broken.
3. true, true, false, true
4. E.g. Yes, because he often knows how to solve problems and proposes solutions that improve life on the island or increase the boys' chances of being rescued, like moving the fire to the beach. **Or** e.g. No, because he does not command the respect of the other boys and has difficulty explaining his ideas to the group so that the boys will see the benefits of these ideas.

Task: Here are some points you could have included:
* Piggy uses logic to dismiss the other boys' fears, such as when he tells Ralph that there can't be ghosts because the human world would not "make sense" if there were.
* Piggy thinks about the practicalities of living on the island, such as the need to build shelters and keep track of time, which highlights his role as the most rational boy in the group.
* Golding often refers to Piggy's glasses when Piggy is trying to use logic. Golding uses the deteriorating state of Piggy's glasses in the novel to symbolise the decline of the boys' use of reason and logic.

Page 18: Jack

1. a) E.g. "He didn't say. He got angry"
   b) E.g. "He's going to beat Wilfred."
   c) E.g. "You're always scared. Yah – Fatty!"
2. E.g. Yes, because he encourages the boys to feast, dance and hunt as much as they like. This suggests that he wants the other boys to enjoy being in his tribe. **Or** e.g. No, because he bullies and tortures the twins and beats Wilfred for no reason, even though they are all part of his tribe. This suggests that he doesn't care whether the other boys are having fun as long as he has power over them.
3. E.g. The fact that he starts to cry and runs off from the rest of the group reveals that his pride is easily hurt if things do not go his way. It also suggests that he likes to be in control of others.
4. E.g. He doesn't want to have to explain what happened on the island because it would mean taking responsibility for his actions.

Task: Here are some points you could have included:
* In Chapter One, he is "tall, thin, and bony" and is smartly dressed in a long black cloak and a cap that covers his red hair. He has pale blue eyes and a freckled face that is "ugly without silliness".
* In Chapter Eleven, Jack's freckled face is concealed by a "green and black mask" of paint and he is only "identifiable by personality and red hair" to Ralph.

Page 19: Simon

1. timid, generous, alone, affecting, Jesus
2. E.g. It makes him seem weaker and more vulnerable than the other characters, which makes the reader more sympathetic towards him.

Answers

3.	E.g. Simon is able to follow a "just perceptible path" through the forest, which suggests that he is aware of subtle variations in his natural surroundings. / His narrative perspective shows that he is constantly observing sights and sounds around him, such as the barely audible "undertone" of the sea breaking on the reef "miles away".

4.	E.g. Words like "stumbled" show that Simon is helpless, making the other boys' attack with "teeth and claws" seem especially brutal. This makes the reader more sympathetic towards Simon.

Task:	Here are some points you could have included:
- Caring attitude towards the littluns shows kind nature
  - Chapter Three: Simon finds the "choicest" fruit and passes it to "endless" hands.
  - Extreme language, e.g. superlative "choicest" = Simon carefully selecting best fruit, suggests he genuinely cares about littluns' wellbeing. Also adjective "endless" = spends lots of his time helping them.
  - Simon's behaviour conforms to image in adventure stories of boys co-existing happily = implies some people do have goodness that these novels suggest exists in people.
- Kindness shown through his treatment of Piggy
  - Chapter Four: Simon gives "his piece of meat" to Piggy when Jack withholds food from Piggy.
  - Gives up his own food = act of generosity that contrasts with Jack's cruelty. Shows kindness is stronger than fear of Jack.
  - Chapter Two: speaks up for Piggy when Jack says he "just sat" rather than making the fire. Transition from speaking for Piggy to acting against Jack for him = Simon's display of kindness increases despite risk.
- Shown to be kind through relationship with Ralph
  - Chapter Six: Ralph just looks at Simon "impatiently" when he walks into a tree. Chapter Seven: Simon tells Ralph he'll "get back all right".
  - Structure: having these two events close together emphasises contrast between Ralph's lack of compassion and Simon's kindness.
  - Chapter Three: relationship with littluns, e.g. picks them the fruit they can't reach = links Simon to Jesus (who said "Suffer the little children to come unto me"). Link foreshadows Simon's sacrificial death later in the book.

Page 20: Roger

1.	E.g. He becomes more aggressive and violent as the novel progresses, especially after joining Jack's savage tribe. / He becomes Jack's closest ally, which gives him a more prominent position in the group.

2.	E.g. Yes, because he obeys the rules of civilised society instead of acting on his desire to hurt Henry, even though there is nobody there to stop him. This suggests that he has not yet lost his civilised values. **Or** e.g. No, because Roger's desires are uncivilised. He only follows the rules of civilisation because he fears punishment, not because he believes that they are good rules to follow.

3.	E.g. It makes him seem more savage, as he expresses himself through violent actions instead of using words.

4.	E.g. He prefers Jack because he encourages brutality and lets him be savage. This makes Roger seem more dangerous to the reader, as it suggests that he thrives on violence.

5.	E.g. To emphasise Roger's transition from a civilised boy to a savage person who is capable of committing extreme violence. / The fact that violent characters are acting on their own initiative, instead of being commanded by Jack, makes the tribe seem more dangerous.

Task:	You should have written your answer in the style of a newspaper report with a relevant headline.
Here are some points you could have included:
- Roger destroys the littluns' sand castles in Chapter Four.
- In Chapter Seven, he fights to get to Robert during the hunting dance so that he can hurt him.
- Roger kills a pig with brutal force in Chapter Eight.
- He murders Piggy in Chapter Eleven.
- He tortures Sam and Eric in Chapters Eleven and Twelve.

Here are some quotes you could have used:
- "Roger, uncommunicative by nature"
- "You don't know Roger. He's a terror."
- "Roger who carried death in his hands"

Page 21: The Littluns

1.	a)	True: e.g. "They talk and scream. The littluns."
	b)	False: e.g. "They obeyed the summons of the conch"

2.	E.g. Roger and Maurice destroy the littluns' sand castles.

3.	E.g. They are "hopeless" at helping out because they quickly lose interest in gathering wood and making shelters.

4.	E.g. It makes them easy to manipulate. For example, Jack convinces them to join his tribe by promising food and protection.

5.	E.g. The littluns lose their sense of civilisation as the novel progresses. They stop caring about hygiene, which suggests that they have forgotten how to be civilised, and Percival completely forgets his name and address by Chapter Twelve.

Page 22: The Other Characters

1.	a)	E.g. "What d'you mean by not joining my tribe?"
	b)	E.g. "You lemme go — / — and me."
	c)	E.g. "one terrified mind between them"

2.	E.g. He falls off the log, which shows that he can be funny and wants to amuse people. / He speaks at the meeting and gets his point across about the squid, which shows that he is articulate.

3.	E.g. They blindly follow Jack's orders, even if it means they must be violent towards one another. / They're afraid of what will happen if they disobey Jack. / They've become more savage, as they're comfortable with the idea of committing acts of violence, even against one of their own friends.

4.	The dead airman: E.g. He falls onto the mountain, scaring Sam and Eric, and then Ralph, Jack and Roger, who all think he is the beast. To show that the boys' fear of the beast is irrational and to show that there is a war going on beyond the island.
	The naval officer: E.g. He rescues Ralph from Jack's tribe and the boys from the island.
	He reminds the reader that the boys are returning to a violent world and that even those people who look civilised can have a savage side.

Page 23: Skills Focus — Making Links

1.	You could have used the following examples:
	Ralph — He sets rules for the others to follow. / He makes sure that the fire is kept burning so that they can be rescued.
	Jack — He finds it humiliating when the boys don't choose him to be chief. / When he is chief, he shouts at any boys who say things he doesn't like.
	The littluns — They eat unripe fruit that gives them stomach ache and diarrhoea. / Jack manipulates them into joining his tribe by promising that he will protect them from the beast.

2.	You could have made the following points:
	Piggy — He is logical, e.g. He suggests making a sundial to allow the boys to keep track of the time. / He suggests building the fire on the beach so they can avoid the beast but still have a better chance of rescue.
	Roger — He is cruel, e.g. He kicks over the littluns' castles. / He tortures Sam and Eric.
	Simon — He is kind to others, e.g. He gives the littluns fruit that is beyond their reach. / He gives Piggy his helping of food when Jack refuses to give Piggy any.

Page 24: Practice Questions

Your answers should have an introduction, several paragraphs developing different ideas and a conclusion. You may have covered some of the following points:

1.	- Jack is presented as a cruel character through the way he treats Piggy. In Chapter Four, when Piggy is winded and sits down to recover, Jack stands "over him". The difference in height between the two characters suggests that Jack is using his position of strength to deliberately intimidate Piggy. Golding structures this part of the novel so that Jack's cruelty is

Answers

highlighted just after some of his hunters agree with Piggy that Jack should not have let the fire go out. This implies that Jack's treatment of Piggy may actually be a result of his own insecurity.

- Golding uses Jack's actions as chief to present him as cruel. In Chapter Ten, Robert implies twice that Jack intends to beat Wilfred without having a reason. This repetition highlights the idea that Jack enjoys inflicting pain, which makes him seem sadistic. Jack's cruelty reflects the behaviour of Adolf Hitler, who ordered the slaughter of millions of people during the Second World War simply for belonging to certain groups in society that he disliked.

- Golding uses Jack's obsession with hunting to present his cruelty. In Chapter Four, when Jack's mind is "crowded" by memories of killing a pig, he remembers that taking its life was like a "long satisfying drink". This suggests that Jack has a thirst for violence that is only sated by blood, implying that killing is one of his basic instincts. The way Jack revels in satisfying this desire highlights his cruelty. In Chapter Eight, Jack's first act as chief is to lead a brutal hunt of a sow and her young, which hints that he is now free to behave as cruelly as he wishes.

2. • Golding uses Ralph to explore the theme of civilisation in the novel. In Chapter Two, Ralph says that the "Queen's got a picture of this island". This reminds the boys that the island has been mapped and is known to Britain, so it is therefore not as isolated from civilisation as it seems to be. Ralph's conviction that the Queen has a map of the island reflects the fact that, before the Second World War, British people founded various overseas colonies and tried to 'civilise' those who already lived there. This reminds the reader that Ralph comes from a country that values civilisation highly.

- Ralph's struggle to create a civilised society plays an important role in Golding's aim of writing a more realistic version of *The Coral Island*. In *The Coral Island*, the main characters find setting up a civilised society on the island easy, but in *Lord of the Flies*, Ralph lives in a world of "baffled common-sense". The juxtaposition of the word "baffled" and the concept of "common-sense" highlights Ralph's struggle to recreate a sensible adult society that he doesn't fully understand. This offers a more realistic idea of how children might manage without adults. This implies that creating a stable society is not as easy as traditional adventure stories suggest.

- Ralph's narrative viewpoint is used to suggest that violence can destroy a person's innocence. Golding structures the novel so that, in Chapter Seven, just before he takes part in his first hunt, Ralph reminisces about life with "Mummy" and "Daddy" in a "cottage on the edge of the moors". These titles encourage the reader to imagine Ralph as a young and innocent child just before he commits an act of violence that suggests that he has lost this innocence. In Chapter Ten, Ralph is unsettled by the same memory because the "attraction of wildness" has gone, implying that his experiences have also tainted his memories of childhood.

3. • The littluns are significant as they allow Golding to explore ideas about fear. In Chapter Two, the littluns introduce the idea of the beast, which is visible at night and turns "into them things like ropes in the trees" in the morning. The littluns' belief that the beast literally becomes the "ropes" underlines how irrational their fear actually is, as the reader knows that the 'beast' has always just been harmless tree vines. The littluns' irrational fear contributes to the downfall of Ralph's civilised society on the island, as Jack exploits the boys' fear to encourage them to join his tribe instead.

- The littluns are important because they show the impact of the breakdown of civilisation. In Chapter Five, Percival's "incantation" of his address is "powerless to help him". By likening his address to a spell Golding suggests that, in a civilised society, saying this information would almost magically get Percival home. The powerlessness of the spell highlights the lack of civilisation on the island, as it suggests that Percival is lost in a place where there are no friendly adults to help him and the concept of an address has no meaning. Percival's powerlessness reflects the way that many children were separated from their families by the dangers of World War Two.

- The littluns are important because they represent ordinary people. The novel can be seen as an allegory for the world in which the littluns, who lead "aimless and trivial" lives and are "seldom bothered" with the older boys, represent ordinary people. This lack of interest in the biguns' lives reflects that ordinary people care more about having food, shelter and security than they do about the wider world. Later in the novel, the littluns blindly follow Jack in return for food and protection, which emphasises how easily evil can take hold when ordinary people don't pay attention to politics and society as a whole.

4. • Ralph's changing attitude towards Piggy shows how they come to complement one another. In Chapter Five, Ralph adjusts his opinion of Piggy when he realises that Piggy can "go step by step" inside his own head and think in a way that Ralph can't, despite Piggy being "no chief". This reflects Ralph's growing recognition that he needs Piggy's insight to rule well but, as Piggy has no power, his intelligence is only useful if Ralph chooses to act on it, emphasising that Ralph is a more effective leader when he listens to Piggy. This may reflect the way that democratic leaders who listened to their people were valued in the 1950s, particularly in contrast to dictators such as Hitler and Stalin.

- Golding uses Ralph and Piggy's relationship to present Piggy as an outsider. In Chapter Four, he uses the verb "rejoiced" to describe Piggy's happiness when he thinks he has made Ralph smile, emphasising Piggy's exaggerated sense of joy at bonding with Ralph. Just before this, Golding uses Ralph's viewpoint to reveal that he smiles "involuntarily" and thinks Piggy is "dull". Shifting from Ralph's view to Piggy's excessively positive one shows that Piggy is even seen as an outsider by those who appear to like him. Piggy becomes less of an outsider when Ralph defends his right to speak and seeks his advice in Chapter Five, reinforcing the link between their relationship and Piggy's status.

- The relationship between Ralph and Piggy highlights Ralph's leadership skills. After revealing Piggy's nickname, Ralph tries to calm him down by telling him it's better to be "Piggy than Fatty" before apologising. Golding structures this exchange so that Ralph's apology comes just after Jack tells Piggy bluntly that they "don't want" him. The contrast between Ralph's recognition of his wrongdoing and Jack's response highlights Ralph's leadership abilities early in the novel. This redeems Ralph a little in the eyes of the reader, as it shows that he is not malicious like Jack.

5. • Golding presents Simon as a victim of the other boys' savagery. In Chapter Eight, after Simon sees Jack's tribe leaving the pig's head for the beast, flies "without number" find him. The idea that the flies can't be quantified emphasises how many are swarming over Simon's body, suggesting that he is physically suffering as a result of the boys' savage actions. Golding uses this event to foreshadow Simon's death in the next chapter when the other boys surround and kill him, which confirms his vulnerability to the other boys' barbarity.

- Simon is presented as being vulnerable to fear. In Chapter Five, Simon's heartbeats are "choking him" when he tries to speak to the other boys about the beast. Here, it is as if Simon's heart, which is supposed to keep him alive, is actually restricting his oxygen supply. The irony this creates demonstrates the strength of Simon's fear; it is powerful enough to make his own body work against him. The fact that Simon does manage to speak again suggests that, while he is vulnerable to fear, he is able to overcome it for the good of the group.

- Golding presents Simon as vulnerable to Jack's desire for power. In Chapter Six, Ralph reprimands Jack after he names Simon as one of the people he believes should "keep quiet" and "leave deciding things" to others. This implies that Jack would happily deny Simon a voice if Ralph was not there to protect Simon's rights. Jack's attempt to silence Simon and the other boys reflects the way in which Adolf Hitler abused his power by disregarding the rights of certain groups in society before and during the Second World War.

Answers

Section Three — Context and Themes

Page 25: Historical Background to 'Lord of the Flies'

1. Second, Nazi, democracy, murdered, scared
2. E.g. Jack persuades the boys to obey him by promising that he will hunt for food and protect them from the beast. He also uses violence to scare Sam and Eric into joining his tribe.
3. a) E.g. Piggy says that people have been killed by an "atom bomb".
   b) E.g. The boys split into two groups — one is led by Jack, who acts like a dictator, and one by Ralph, who has been elected.
   c) E.g. Ralph describes the island as "All ours." / Ralph, Jack and Simon "savoured the right of domination" when they explored the island.
   d) E.g. Jack thinks that English people are the "best at everything".

Page 26: Social Background to 'Lord of the Flies'

1. false, true, true, false
2. a) E.g. "Wearily obedient, the choir huddled into line"
   b) E.g. "intimidated by this uniformed superiority"
3. E.g. The boys lose their self-control and give in to their barbaric instincts when they kill Simon. In contrast, upper-class boys were expected to be restrained and self-disciplined.
4. E.g. Jack, who is one of the most privileged characters, is also one of the cruellest and most violent. Piggy, who is from a lower social class, is principled and kind.

Page 27: Civilisation and Barbarity

1. b) E.g. The boys stop tending to the fire as they concentrate on hunting.
   c) E.g. The boys become anonymous savages when they paint themselves. / Percival has forgotten his name by the end of the novel.
2. E.g. At first, the boys wear school uniforms, which symbolise their civilised upbringing. Later, they paint their faces, which makes them look like "savages" and symbolises their rejection of civilised values.
3. E.g. When he is still part of Ralph's group, Jack says "Bollocks to the rules!" and speaks without holding the conch, which shows that he doesn't value the rules and won't obey them.
4. E.g. He is suggesting that anybody is capable of acting barbarically. The fact that the boys kill Simon with "teeth and claws" suggests they are acting like animals.
Task: Your answer will vary depending on the point in the novel you chose. If you chose the point when most of the boys join Jack's tribe in Chapter Eight, your points might include:
- By joining Jack's tribe, the boys show that they now value hunting over more civilised goals such as building shelters and trying to get rescued.
- This is a shift from the start of the novel, when building a signal fire to attract a ship was their main goal.
- It also suggests that the majority of the boys are now more drawn to Jack's violent, unpredictable leadership than to Ralph's more sensible, fair leadership.
- At this point, the majority of the boys allow their savage side to dominate their civilised side.

Page 28: Fear

1. E.g. "the beast is — a ghost" / "the beast may swing through the trees"
2. E.g. It makes them restless at night, so they stay together "for comfort." It also causes them to join Jack's tribe for protection.
3. E.g. When the beast is first mentioned, he starts laughing and dismisses their fears. Later, he takes them more seriously.
4. E.g. Simon's death is a direct result of the boys' fear of the beast. Their fear makes them act instinctively, and they don't realise that they are attacking Simon until it is too late.
5. E.g. Jack suggests that the beast is "a hunter" that can hurt the boys and calls Ralph a "coward". This implies that Ralph can't protect them, which reduces Ralph's influence over the group.

Page 29: Power and Leadership

1. E.g. He doesn't care about the views of the people he leads and makes decisions that benefit himself rather than others.
2. You should have ticked the second box.
3. E.g. Jack: "the steady fall of his tears"
   Ralph: "You aren't playing the game."
4. a) E.g. "I can't think. Not like Piggy."
   b) E.g. Ralph realises that Piggy can think better than him, showing that he recognises other people's strengths and his own weaknesses. / He adapts what he says and how he speaks to ensure all members of the group understand what he's saying.
5. E.g. Wilfred is punished for no reason, and Roger realises that he can commit violent acts without consequences. This suggests that Golding views Jack's leadership style as unjust and dangerous.
Task: Here are some points you could have included:
- Contrast between leadership styles of Ralph and Jack to show different motives
  - Ralph's rules vs. Jack's "irresponsible authority".
  - Contrasts in leadership reflect contrast in views about responsibility — Ralph wants a civilised society and to return home vs. Jack enjoys power without responsibility.
  - Ralph's more noble motives make him seem more mature and honourable than Jack.
- Important to Golding's message that irresponsible leadership can have dire consequences
  - Jack's leadership leads to the deaths of Simon and Piggy, and turns the island to "burning wreckage".
  - "wreckage" = Jack's leadership has caused destruction. Shows bad leadership can be catastrophic for society.
  - Reinforces message that good leadership is important for the survival of civilisation.
- Ralph and Jack's different styles of leadership show the importance of democracy
  - Ralph is democratically elected and uses democratic rules to organise meetings, e.g. the conch. Jack seizes power and rules as a dictator.
  - Conch symbolises democracy where everyone has a voice. Jack's dictatorship and rejection of conch denies the other boys a voice and causes conflict.
  - Reflects consequences of Hitler's dictatorship in mid-20th century = minority groups persecuted and WWII.

Page 30: Nature

1. E.g. To imply that the boys' experiences on the island will not be as fun and exciting as they believe. This creates tension by suggesting that the island is not as safe as it seems.
2. E.g. The signal fire burns out of control, killing a littlun.
3. E.g. It suggests that it is isolated and vulnerable by emphasising its relatively small size compared to the "miles wide" waves of the ocean that are "disregarding" the island's existence.
4. E.g. He feels comfortable in the natural world and notices small changes in sounds, such as bees buzzing.
5. E.g. Nature has the power to erase damage caused by human acts. Simon's murder only causes temporary damage to the natural world, which shows that nature endures despite human actions.

Page 31: Games

1. a) E.g. "Life became a race with the fire"
   b) E.g. "Assembly after assembly had broken up in laughter"
2. E.g. It foreshadows the point where many boys leave Ralph's group to join Jack's tribe, partly because they'd rather have fun than work.
3. a) E.g. Roger and Maurice kick the sand castles down, knocking sand into Percival's face.
   b) E.g. The boys attack Robert with spears, despite his shouts for them to stop.

Answers

4. E.g. Yes, because the boys' actions stem from games. For example, the boys pretend to kill Robert in a game in the forest, then later end up killing Simon. **Or** e.g. No, because the boys take hunting very seriously, and the disagreement between the two groups goes beyond a game when it becomes violent and leads to deaths.

Exam Practice:

Your answer should have an introduction, several paragraphs developing different ideas and a conclusion. You may have covered some of the following points:

*   Golding presents games as a sign of immaturity. In Chapter One, Ralph initially treats blowing the conch as a game and uses it to make a "low, farting noise" for "some minutes". The way that Ralph and Piggy are distracted from their serious purpose of calling a meeting by this childish game emphasises their youth and lack of maturity. Later in the novel, Ralph's reluctance to blow the conch in case the boys don't obey its summons emphasises his understanding that it is not a toy but something that holds power. This suggests that he has gained maturity since Chapter One.
*   Golding presents children's games as naive to explore ideas about childhood innocence. In the final chapter, Ralph wonders if he might call "pax" to end his conflict with Jack, but soon realises that this would not work. The term "pax" was used by 1950s schoolchildren to secure a truce during games. Ralph's realisation that this playground rule can't protect him from real hostility reveals the innocence of children's games, where conflict can be resolved with one word. The naval officer's assumption in the final chapter that the boys' war is just "Fun and games" reminds the reader that the boys are only children, which makes their violence more shocking.
*   In Chapter Eleven, Golding switches narrative perspective to show how Roger's stone-throwing game escalates to murder. Roger initially throws stones "to miss" the twins, but the knowledge that his game could harm them causes a "power" to "pulse" in Roger, which reaches maturity in the moment of "delirious abandonment" when he kills Piggy. This focus on Roger's emotions highlights how twisted and out of control the boys' games have become. Using Roger's viewpoint also reminds the reader of the earlier scene when he threw stones "to miss" Henry because of the "taboo of the old life", showing that it is Roger's loss of civilised values that has caused his game to become murderous.

Page 32: Evil

1. E.g. "Evening" brings the "threat of violence", which associates the growing darkness on the island with the boys' increasing savagery.
2. E.g. Everyone has evil inside them as even Ralph, a very moral character, is involved in the evil act of killing Simon.
3. You should have ticked the third box.
4. E.g. The Lord of the Flies says that the boys can't "hunt and kill" evil, suggesting that it is impossible to defeat. Simon loses consciousness at the end of the struggle, symbolising the triumph of evil over good.
5. E.g. Yes, because the tribe revert to "little boys" who "sob" when the officer arrives, suggesting that his presence reminds them about civilisation and saves them from their evil actions. **Or** e.g. No, because Ralph cries for "the darkness of man's heart", suggesting that he understands that evil is inside everyone and cannot be overcome or escaped.

Task: Here are some points you could have included:

*   In Chapter Seven, during a hunting dance, Ralph finds the impulse to "hurt" Robert "over-mastering". This suggests that he struggles to control his evil impulses.
*   Ralph feels a "feverish excitement" as well as "loathing" when he remembers Simon's murder. This suggests that part of him found it thrilling to take a life.
*   In Chapter Twelve, Ralph takes the sharpened stick to use as a weapon. He doesn't hesitate before stabbing one of the other boys with it, despite not knowing who it is, hinting that he has been corrupted by their evil behaviour.

Page 33: Skills Focus — Writing about Context

1. a) the dictator Adolf Hitler, who used threats of violence to ensure obedience before and during the Second World War
    b) "matins", a religious service often held in public schools / In the 1950s, some people believed that boys who went to public school gained a greater sense of discipline / clothing and language that are largely exclusive to those with a public school background
2. E.g. In the 1950s, being British was associated with certain moral standards and values that implied good behaviour.

Page 34: Practice Questions

Your answers should have an introduction, several paragraphs developing different ideas and a conclusion. You may have covered some of the following points:

1. *   Golding uses the novel's structure to present fear of the beast as irrational. In Chapter Six, the boys' fear intensifies when the twins describe the beast. Shortly after this, Golding uses Simon's perspective to reveal Simon's "incredulity" that the beast exists. Switching to Simon's logical perspective makes the other boys' fear seem less rational. In the rest of the novel, Piggy, the most rational boy, consistently doubts the beast's existence, reinforcing the idea that fear of the beast is irrational.
    *   Fear is presented as a source of evil in the novel. The boys' "desire" to kill Simon stems from their "terror" of the beast. The word "desire" suggests that the boys feel a strong longing to kill, emphasising that their fear has been twisted into something evil. This links the novel to people's actions during the Second World War, when fear led many people to join the Nazi Party and commit evil acts, such as the murder of millions of Jews in the holocaust.
    *   Golding presents fear as a powerful force in the novel. At the end of Chapter Twelve, the narrator states that Ralph "became fear". This suggests that he is entirely engulfed by fear, implying that it is the only thing he is able to experience. This emphasises the power that fear can have over the human mind and body. Ralph is described using animalistic language in the final chapter — for example he "showed his teeth" and "snarled" — suggesting that fear is powerful enough to strip away his humanity.
2. *   The novel's context influenced Golding's message that the desire for self-preservation can overcome morality. In Chapter Nine, Ralph and Piggy are "eager" to join Jack's "demented but partly secure society". The word "demented" makes Jack's society seem insane and unpredictable, which contradicts the idea that it is "secure". This conflict reflects the fact that many people in Germany in the 1930s and 1940s were able to protect themselves from the Nazi Party by being part of the corrupt and cruel society that it created. The fact that Piggy and Ralph seek the security of Jack's immoral society shows that even good people may abandon their moral values if it will keep them safe.
    *   The evil that Golding witnessed in the Second World War influenced his desire to write a realistic adventure story. In *Lord of the Flies*, Golding emphasises the violent desires and behaviour of Roger and Jack to challenge the suggestion made in R. M. Ballantyne's *The Coral Island* that boys would exist in harmony if there were no rules. This reflects Golding's belief that everyone has evil inside them, which was influenced by the fact that even 'normal' people committed evil acts in the Second World War. Golding's presentation of human nature warns the reader that a civilised person can very easily become barbaric.
    *   The novel's context influenced Golding's exploration of English 'superiority'. In Chapter Two, Jack tells the boys that they need rules, saying "we're not savages. We're English". This emphasises Jack's belief that being "English" and being "savages" are opposing things, which reflects the fact that many English people in the 1950s saw themselves as superior to people from other countries in the British Empire. However, this idea is challenged by the fact that Jack becomes one of the most savage characters in the novel. By countering the concept of English superiority, Golding emphasises that there is barbarity in every society.

Answers

3. • Nature is presented as beautiful in the novel. In Chapter One, Golding uses colours to describe the island, such as when he refers to the lagoon as being "blue of all shades and shadowy green and purple". This gives the impression that the island is a work of art, which emphasises its natural beauty. Later in the novel, Simon uses a "critical ear" to listen to the natural sounds of the island, such as the "undertone" of the sea, as if listening to music. This reinforces the beauty of nature in the novel.

• Nature is presented as bountiful in the novel. In Chapter One, three littluns appear on the beach after "gorging fruit". The word "gorging" suggests that they have been feasting on an endless supply of fruit, implying that nature has provided them with a bountiful source of nutrition. Golding structures this chapter so that the reader already knows that the fruit has caused Piggy to suffer from diarrhoea, which shows that nature's bounty is not as dependable as it appears to be. This hints that life on the island will not be straightforward.

• Golding presents nature as able to regenerate. A "scar" is gouged into the forest by the plane crash, but by Chapter Four, "complex undergrowth" is "engulfing" this scar. The image of the scar being 'engulfed' suggests that nature has wrapped itself in a protective cocoon to heal this damage, highlighting nature's ability to regenerate. The "scar" is reminiscent of the trenches dug by soldiers during the Second World War; by the 1950s, these would have been revegetated and become less recognisable as artefacts of war, reinforcing the idea that nature can repair the damage done by man.

4. • Golding uses Ralph's insistence that the boys follow rules to present civilisation as a form of protection. In Chapter Five, Ralph exclaims that the rules are the "only thing we've got!" The use of the adjective "only" emphasises that the rules are the last thing left from the civilised world, which reflects Ralph's belief that they are the sole barrier between the boys and barbarity. Golding structures this chapter so that, immediately after Ralph's exclamation, Jack rejects the rules and the assembly descends into chaos, implying that civilisation only offers protection if people follow its rules.

• Ralph represents civilised values, so the other boys' changing attitude towards him reflects their attitude towards civilisation. In Chapter One, Ralph is elected leader mainly because of his association with the conch, which symbolises civilisation. However, in Chapter Eight, most of the boys abandon Ralph and join Jack. Their rejection of Ralph as a leader symbolises their rejection of civilisation. In Chapter Eleven, Golding reinforces the idea that the power of civilisation has decreased, as even Ralph forgets the importance of the smoke signal.

• Golding uses Ralph's daydreams to present civilisation as a means of mastering nature. In Chapter Ten, Ralph associates safety with a bus station and "its lamps and wheels" while fantasising about a "tamed town". The inventions of "lamps and wheels" overcome natural obstacles like darkness and rough terrain, so linking them with 'taming' emphasises that human civilisation imposes order on nature. Ralph's mindset reflects western values in the mid-20th century, when technological advances in areas such as transport and building increased people's power over nature, giving a sense that they were 'overcoming' the natural world.

5. • Golding presents power as dangerous when it is abused. In Chapter Nine, Jack uses his power to whip the boys into a frenzy by commanding them to dance and chant, but their chant soon loses its "superficial excitement" and begins to "beat like a steady pulse". The speed with which the chant changes from a "superficial" thing manufactured by Jack into something with a "pulse" that has a life of its own emphasises that Jack has created a situation that he can't control. Golding structures this chapter so that Simon's death occurs just after Jack initiates this chaos, confirming that abuse of power has dangerous consequences.

• Golding presents democratic power as superior to the power of a dictator. Ralph, who uses his power to create a fair society, is elected by the "acclaim" of the boys, emphasising that he rules by consent of others. In contrast, Jack seizes power with the abrupt statement that he is "going to be chief" and is shown

to be a cruel leader through his use of violence. This contrast encourages the audience to see the power of an elected leader as better for society than power taken by force. The conflict over leadership between Ralph and Jack reflects the hostility between democracies and dictatorships during the Cold War; Golding may have intended the destruction caused by the war between the boys as a warning about the dangers of outright war between the east and the west.

• Power is presented as something that can be suppressed. In Chapter Eight, when Jack leaves the group, Piggy's influence grows and he feels a sense of "expanding liberty". The word "expanding" suggests that Piggy's freedom has been restricted and has now been released and allowed to grow, emphasising that his power to express himself and contribute to the group had previously been suppressed by Jack. Golding structures the events of this chapter so that Piggy's suggestion about moving the fire is put into action by the group shortly after Jack's departure, which reinforces the link between Jack's absence and Piggy's ability to exercise power.

Section Four — The Writer's Techniques

Page 35: Form in 'Lord of the Flies'

1. E.g. Ralph, Jack and Simon enjoy exploring the island, and they discover that it is most likely deserted. This confirms that the boys are in a remote place without adult supervision.

2. b) E.g. The boys think there is a beast in the trees. Their fear of it never goes away and contributes to Simon's death.
   c) E.g. No one prevents the torture of Wilfred and the twins, and the boys hunt Ralph at the end of the novel.

3. E.g. Golding shows boys from a 'civilised' background becoming savage, which reflects his belief that everyone has a barbaric side.

4. E.g. The boys initially form a democracy, but this is replaced by the tribe — a dictatorship ruled by Jack — which almost all the boys eventually become part of. By the end, only Ralph still seems to value democracy at all.

Page 36: Structure and Viewpoint

1. Event: Fire spreads across the island at the end of the novel, threatening Ralph.
   Explanation: e.g. It makes the reader believe that Ralph may also be killed by the fire, which creates tension.

2. E.g. It implies that time is unimportant to the boys' lives on the island, which shows that they're losing touch with civilisation.

3. E.g. It suggests that they don't know the characters and are learning about them at the same time as the reader. This suggests that they won't be biased.

4. E.g. It highlights the way that the boys are acting as a mob and makes it seem as though they are all responsible for Simon's death.

5. E.g. It creates suspense by making the reader wonder whether the twins will arrive safely back at camp and making them anticipate the effect that the twins' news about the beast will have.

Page 37: Language — How the Characters Speak

1. E.g. They use slang words like "Wizard" and "Smashing" that would have been heard in schools in the 1950s. / They shout "Whee-aa-oo" and describe a boulder as a "bomb", which makes them seem excitable and playful.

2. E.g. In Chapter One the boys are generally polite, but from Chapter Four onwards, they begin to use violent chants such as *Kill the pig.* This gives the reader the impression that they have changed from innocent boys to violent savages.

3. a) E.g. Piggy uses non-standard English, including double negatives like "there isn't no beast", whereas the other boys use standard English.
   b) Piggy is less well-spoken than the others, which suggests that he has had a less privileged education and upbringing. / It suggests that he comes from a different background to the other boys, which makes him seem like an outsider.

Answers

4. E.g. "Then there was, there was..."
    Any valid explanation, e.g. The repetition of "there was" makes his speech sound muddled, and the ellipsis shows that he is pausing. This suggests he doesn't know what to say.

Task: Here are some points you may have included:
* Phil describes vines in the trees as "twisty things". This suggests that he isn't yet old enough to have learned the correct name for the vines.
* His speech is full of short phrases that are connected by the basic conjunction "and", suggesting that his vocabulary is still very limited.

Pages 38-39: Language — The Writer's Effects

1. a) E.g. Jack later encourages the other boys to abandon the rules and becomes the chief of a tribe of "savages", which is the opposite of his earlier attitude.
    b) E.g. Simon is mistaken for the beast as he comes to tell the other boys that there is no beast. / The smoke from the fire intended to drive Ralph to his death causes the boys' rescue.

2. a) E.g. Glasses are associated with sight and clarity, making them a good symbol for logical thinking. / Piggy continues to think rationally even when the other boys have lost their reason.
    b) E.g. The boys' loss of reason as they become increasingly savage. / Piggy's death in Chapter Eleven. / The destruction of the conch.

3. Explanation: E.g. Golding describes the island in unreal terms, as a place of magical "illusions", while descriptions like "pearl and opalescence" make it seem like a beautiful paradise.
    Effect: E.g. It makes the reader feel that nothing on the island is as it seems, which creates a sense of unease.

4. E.g. Referring to them as "the hunters" shows how quickly their civilised values are replaced by their primitive desires, while calling them "savages" shows that they have completely rejected civilisation in favour of violence.

5. Repetition: E.g. It emphasises the size of the swell and makes the waves seem more powerful.
    Personification: E.g. "The flames were mastering the branches". It makes it seem like the fire is taking over, which creates a sense of danger and the boys' powerlessness. / "the trees of the forest sighed, then roared". It makes the forest seem angry, which gives the impression that it is the boys' enemy.
    Simile: E.g. "Something flittered there in front of his mind like a bat's wing". This suggests that Ralph's mind is being troubled by something intrusive and dark.

6. E.g. Golding uses long sentences, such as "There were miles of vague water... shaft of a pit" when Ralph is approaching the twins, which emphasises his slow movements and slows the pace. / The twins use lots of short, unfinished phrases like "— and the Chief — they're both —". This makes their dialogue sound hurried, which increases the pace of this part of the novel.

7. a) E.g. The word "silvered" makes Simon seem like a shining light, while "marble" is often white, linking it to purity. / Silver and marble are valuable materials that can be used for sculptures, making Simon's body seem like a memorial to a hero.
    b) E.g. It makes Simon's violent death seem even sadder to the reader by highlighting his goodness and pure heart. / It suggests that nature is mourning Simon's death, which increases the sense of loss.

Exam Practice:
Your answer should have an introduction, several paragraphs developing different ideas and a conclusion. You may have covered some of the following points:
* Golding uses descriptive language to create a threatening atmosphere. In Chapter Nine, he uses the verb "brooded" to personify the clouds above the island, which makes them seem angry and unsettled. This suggests that there is a malevolent force hanging over the island that might unleash something terrible, which creates an ominous atmosphere. This atmosphere remains until the end of the chapter, when Golding uses descriptive language to create a peaceful mood after Simon's death. This change implies that Simon's murder was the terrible event that was being foreshadowed.

* Golding uses setting to create a threatening atmosphere in Chapter One. Just after Piggy says he and Ralph might be on the island until they "die", the narrator states "With that word the heat" intensified until it was "a threatening weight". This creates a threatening mood by associating the island's oppressive heat with death, which implies that the boys are trapped in a hostile place. The emphasis on "die" heightens this sense of threat, as it hints that the boys are truly at risk of death, unlike in traditional adventure stories where the characters can overcome the obstacles they face.
* Golding uses references to the war in the 'adult world' to create a threatening atmosphere. In Chapter Six, an aerial battle takes place above the island at "ten miles" height. Locating the battle far above the island implies that the war overshadows the boys' lives even while they are isolated on the island, which reflects the inescapable threat that the Cold War posed to the world in the mid-20th century. This emphasises the danger that the adult world poses to the boys, which intensifies the threatening mood. The dead airman's arrival on the island ultimately leads to Simon's murder, which confirms the threat the war poses to the boys' lives, heightening the novel's threatening atmosphere.

Page 40: Skills Focus — Close Language Analysis

1. Piece of close language analysis: 2
    Explanation of choice: The analysis of the term "islanded" explains exactly how this description emphasises Piggy's sense of isolation.

2. b) E.g. The word "tide" suggests that the boys act as a single, powerful force. The fact that Roger isn't drawn back by it shows he is independent.
    c) E.g. The word "swarmed" suggests the boys are anonymous, possibly deadly, and numerous, like insects in a swarm.

Page 41: Practice Questions

Your answers should have an introduction, several paragraphs developing different ideas and a conclusion. You may have covered some of the following points:

1.
* Piggy is presented as an outsider through the way that his voice is suppressed. In Chapter Two, he repeatedly says "I got the conch" while trying to make the others listen. The fact that he has to appeal several times to the power of the conch, which should give him the right to speak, shows that the boys don't respect the rules when it comes to Piggy. This emphasises his status as an outsider early in the novel. Piggy's use of non-standard English suggests that he is from a lower social class than the other boys. Class divides were strong in the UK in the 1950s, which implies that Piggy's background is a reason for his exclusion from the group.
* Piggy is presented as an outsider through Simon's death. When Simon is killed, the boys dance in "complementary circles" that become a "single organism", but Ralph later says that Piggy was "Outside the circle". Likening the circles of boys to a "single organism" suggests the boys are acting as one living being. Piggy's position "outside" this circle highlights his exclusion from this group. The fact that Simon, another outsider, is killed by this "organism" implies Piggy's status as an outsider may prove to be fatal.
* Golding presents Piggy as an outsider through the way he clings to the adult world. Piggy considers what "grown-ups" will think of Simon's murder and often refers to his "auntie". The fact that he wants to stay connected to his old life ruled by adults, while the rest of the boys enjoy their freedom, suggests that he is different from them. Before he dies, Piggy repeats his line from Chapter Two that the boys are "a crowd of kids", which implies that he is still the only boy who considers their behaviour from an adult perspective.

2.
* Golding adapts the adventure story form to introduce a menacing atmosphere early in the novel. In Chapter Two, he uses the boys' references to exciting 19th-century adventure stories like *Treasure Island* to suggest that they are having a fun adventure, but at the end of the chapter a littlun dies.

64

Answers

In adventure stories, the characters normally overcome peril, so this change of atmosphere goes against the reader's expectations and shows that the boys are in mortal danger. The fact that it is a littlun who dies suggests that the most innocent boys may be most at risk, which heightens this new atmosphere of menace.

- Golding uses changes in setting to create a darker atmosphere as the story progresses. In Chapter Four, "floods of light" bathe the island in "pearl" and "opalescence". This imagery of bright light and iridescent colour creates a heavenly atmosphere. However, in Chapter Twelve, Piggy's and Simon's deaths are described as a "vapour" hanging over the island. The word "vapour" implies that the island is shrouded in mist as a result of the boys' evil. This creates a dark atmosphere that contrasts with the lighter mood in Chapter Four. This change reflects the way the boys become more savage as they commit increasingly evil acts.
- Golding uses dialogue to create an increasingly tense atmosphere as the novel progresses. In Chapter One, Ralph defuses tension between himself and Jack by saying that the choir "belongs" to Jack, whereas by Chapter Four Ralph is so angry that he can only speak in short, accusatory sentences such as "You let the fire out." This builds tension by suggesting that Ralph is no longer willing to pacify Jack, hinting at the confrontation to come. At the end of the novel, Ralph seems to lose his grasp on language and communicates by "screaming, snarling". This heightens the tension by suggesting that Ralph will not be able to reason with the tribe.

3.
- Golding builds repeated hunting scenes into the novel's structure to present the boys' increasing savagery. In the first hunting scene, Jack fails to kill a pig because the idea of blood is "unbearable", but after the next hunt, he describes "lashings of blood". The word "lashings" is often used to describe large amounts of sauce or gravy, so its use here suggests that, rather than being repulsed by blood, Jack is almost savouring it. This change in Jack's attitude shows that he has become more at ease with savage acts. After a later hunting scene, Jack laughs at blood on his hands, showing how quickly savagery can become acceptable.
- Animal imagery is used to present savage behaviour. When Jack's hunters attack Ralph and Piggy, they are heard "prowling" around the shelter before starting a fight full of "biting" and "scratching". The word "prowling" suggests that the boys are predators stalking their prey, while the "scratching" and "biting" makes their violence seem animalistic, which suggests that it is instinctive. The destruction in this fight of the shelter, which symbolises civilisation, reinforces Golding's idea that giving in to savage instincts can destabilise society.
- Savage behaviour is presented as part of human nature. In Chapter Eleven, Ralph's group fears Jack's "painted" tribe because they think that "concealing paint" brings "liberation into savagery". This implies that their war paint conceals the civilised identity that the boys display to society and allows them to reveal their inner savagery. Golding uses this symbolism to reflect the fact that many countries sanctioned atrocious acts of violence during the Second World War, which reinforces the message that savagery exists even within supposedly civilised societies.

4.
- Golding uses different narrative perspectives to create suspense. In Chapter Four, Roger doesn't throw stones directly at Henry because of the "invisible" protection of "parents and school and policemen", suggesting that he still feels governed by the authorities of his old life. Just after this, the narrator says that the "civilisation" that protects Henry is in "ruins". This creates suspense as the reader wonders what will happen when Roger realises that Henry is unprotected. This suspense is heightened later in the chapter when Jack fails to notice a "darker shadow" that the narrator observes within Roger.
- Ralph's childhood memories are used to create suspense in Chapter Seven. While taking part in a hunt, Ralph remembers the *Mammoth Book for Boys*, a book of adventure stories from the mid-20th century, and observes that "everything was good-humoured and friendly". Placing this memory within

the hunting scene creates suspense as it hints that Ralph's adventure will not be fun and exciting like those in the stories from his childhood. Adventure stories were popular with children in the 1950s, when the novel was published, so many readers would have been familiar with them. This would have made the events of the novel more unexpected and shocking.
- Golding uses sentence structure to create suspense. When Jack's tribe hunt Ralph, Ralph sees a savage's knees appear, followed by "Two hands. A spear." and "A face." This makes it seem as though the boy is appearing before the reader in real-time as more of him becomes visible to Ralph, while the full stops create a regular rhythm, as if imitating a rapid heartbeat. This creates suspense by putting the reader in Ralph's position, only revealing what he sees and feels. Just after this, the narrative moves to the savage's viewpoint, which increases the suspense as the reader waits to see if Ralph has been seen.

5.
- Golding uses the novel's structure to mirror the traditional adventure story form. The novel ends with the boys being 'rescued' by the naval officer. This structure reflects that of adventure stories, which often end with the characters being saved, having suffered no lasting damage. However, Ralph's weeping "for the end of innocence" when he is rescued shows that he has been permanently scarred by his experiences. This adaptation of the adventure story form reflects Golding's intention to create a more realistic version of novels like *The Coral Island*.
- Golding uses the order of different narrative perspectives to present characters' evil intentions. When Roger is throwing stones at Henry, Roger's viewpoint shows that he has an immoral desire to hurt Henry. Roger's perspective is followed immediately by Henry's perspective on the same event; Henry believes that a "friend" is just "teasing him". This structure emphasises Henry's misinterpretation of Roger's violent motives. This would have seemed particularly relevant to readers in the 1950s, as Henry's ignorance mirrors the fact that the full extent of Hitler's evil motives during the 1930s and 1940s didn't become completely clear to the general public until later.
- Golding uses the novel's time scheme to explore the theme of civilisation and barbarity. Bill is so savage in Chapter Twelve that he no longer matches Ralph's "ancient picture" of him as "a boy in shorts and shirt". The image of "shorts and shirt" refers to Chapter One when the boys wore school uniform. Using the word "ancient" to describe this part of the novel suggests that the days when Bill was civilised are part of a dead, historic time, implying that he can never truly return to civilisation. This warns the reader of the consequences of allowing savage behaviour to exist in a civilised society.

Section Five — Exam Buster

Page 42: Understanding the Question

1. b) <u>What</u> is the <u>significance</u> of <u>Simon</u> in *Lord of the Flies*?
   c) <u>Explain</u> <u>how</u> the theme of <u>barbarity</u> is <u>explored</u> in *Lord of the Flies*.
   d) <u>How</u> does Golding <u>create</u> <u>tension</u> in *Lord of the Flies*?
   e) <u>Explain</u> <u>how</u> the <u>importance</u> of <u>good leadership</u> is <u>explored</u> in the novel.
   f) <u>How</u> is the character of <u>Ralph</u> <u>presented</u> in the novel?
   g) <u>Explain</u> <u>why</u> <u>the boys</u> <u>change</u> in *Lord of the Flies*.
2. a - 5, b - 1, c - 4, d - 2, e - 3

Page 43: Making a Rough Plan

1. E.g. He shows the reader the qualities of a bad leader. / The conflict between him and Ralph creates tension. / He helps to convey the idea that people from higher social classes aren't superior to others. / His obsession with hunting helps drive the events of the novel.

Answers

Answers

2. Pick your three most important points and put them in a sensible order. Write down a quote or an example from the novel that backs them up.

Page 44: Making Links

1. Violence is a feature of Jack's leadership. E.g. Jack's tribe hunts Ralph with spears in the last chapter.
   Violence increases as the novel progresses. E.g. Roger's game of throwing stones around Henry develops into him killing Piggy with a rock.
   Violence exists in the outside world as well as on the island. E.g. Piggy tells Ralph about the "atom bomb" in Chapter One.
2. E.g. If one of your points was 'The conflict between him and Ralph creates tension' and your evidence was that in Chapter Three Ralph and Jack argue over whether building huts or hunting is more important, you could link it to the fact that in Chapter Eleven their conflict comes to a head when they fight and Jack wounds Ralph with his spear.

Page 45: Structuring Your Answer

1. Point: Golding uses the boys' appearance to show that they become more savage as the novel progresses.
   Example: When Jack is first introduced, he is wearing a school uniform, but he quickly begins to hunt wearing only "tattered shorts".
   Explain: Jack's uniform represents the discipline of his previous life, so the fact that it gets torn suggests that his civilised values are fading.
   Develop: The idea that the boys' appearance reflects their increasing barbarity is echoed when Jack begins to paint his face, which provides a "liberation into savagery".
2. a) The Lord of the Flies tells Simon that evil is "part of" him.
   b) Piggy claims that Simon's death was an "accident".
3. E.g. Point: Jack shows the reader the qualities of a bad leader.
   Example: He exclaims "Sucks to the littluns!"
   Explain: This shows that he doesn't care about the littluns' welfare.
   Develop: This is also shown through the way he doesn't help to build huts, even though he knows this would comfort the younger boys.

Page 46: Introductions and Conclusions

1. Intro b) is better, e.g. Intro a) makes points which aren't relevant to the question, such as the reference to Piggy's loyalty.
2. E.g. The first sentence should be made relevant to the question by mentioning Piggy's intelligence. No new points should be introduced — the conclusion should give a summary of the points already made in the essay.
Task: Your introduction and conclusion should both give a clear answer to the question. The introduction should include your main points, but no evidence. Your conclusion should summarise your argument and not include new points.

Page 47: Writing about Context

1. a - 2, b - 1, c - 3
2. Contextual information: The idea that a nuclear attack would have terrible consequences reflects the fear of conflict breaking out between the USA and the USSR during the Cold War; both countries had nuclear weapons which had the potential to cause large-scale destruction.
   You could have included context as the Explain or Develop part of the paragraph. The context you wrote about should be relevant to your Point and linked to the Example.

Page 48: Linking Ideas and Paragraphs

1. E.g. The other boys treat Piggy unkindly. For example, Ralph doesn't apologise for revealing Piggy's nickname to the others at first, instead saying that it's "Better Piggy than Fatty". This shows that he doesn't respect Piggy. In this way, Golding shows that people with a privileged background are not necessarily always kind or moral.

2. You should have used the P.E.E.D. structure and included connecting words and phrases such as 'therefore' or 'for example' to link your ideas.
3. E.g. Golding also uses the character of Jack to...
   This idea is developed further when...

Page 49: Marking Answer Extracts

1. 4-5: The answer gives a thoughtful personal response to the text and shows an understanding of contextual factors. However, the analysis of Golding's language isn't detailed enough for it to be a 6-7 answer. There are some spelling and punctuation errors, and the range of vocabulary and sentence structures is limited.

Page 50: Marking Answer Extracts

1. a) 8-9: E.g. "The word "over-mastering"... impulse to hurt others." — closely and perceptively analyses how the writer uses language
   "The boys' situation... action or decision." — detailed exploration of the relationship between the text and its context
   b) 6-7: E.g. "In Chapter Six... "wizard fort"." — integrated, well-chosen example
   "By imagining the path... an exciting adventure." — thorough exploration of how the writer uses language

Pages 51-52: Marking a Whole Answer

1. 8-9: E.g. The answer examines several different aspects of context in detail, including the British Empire and World War Two, and Golding's views on these. There is close and perceptive analysis of form, for example the examination of Golding's use of the adventure story form in the second paragraph.

Page 53: Skills Focus — Writing Well

1. The conch is a cymbal [symbol] which represents civilisation. It is initally [initially] a practical tool that is used to call meetings and indicate when a boy is allowed to speak, with all of the boys respecting it's [its] status. However, as the novel progresses, the power of the conch begins to dissappear [disappear] as the boys [boys'] barbaric instincts take over from there [their] regard for the rules on the island. Eventually, the conch is smashed into a "thousand white fragments", reflecting Jack's tribe's complete abandonment of civilisation when they intentionly [intentionally] murder Piggy.
2. You could have rewritten the sentences as follows:
   a) The fact that Piggy has glasses makes him seem cleverer than the other boys.
   b) The weather helps to create a frightening atmosphere during the dance where Simon is killed.
   c) Simon appears to enjoy spending time away from the other boys.
   d) The littluns often cry and become obsessed with the beast.

Page 54: Practice Questions

Your answers should have an introduction, several paragraphs developing different ideas and a conclusion. You may have covered some of the following points:

1. • Golding uses Simon to suggest that behaving in a morally good way makes people vulnerable. For example, in Chapter Nine, Simon decides to do the 'right' thing by disobeying the Lord of the Flies and telling the other boys that the beast isn't real. However, his determination to do this is what makes him enter the dance, leading to his violent death. The idea that moral behaviour can make people vulnerable is reinforced through the character of Piggy; Piggy's passionate speech in favour of democratic values comes just before he is killed by Roger.
   • Golding uses the confrontation between Simon and the pig's head to suggest that evil is within everyone. After their conversation, in which the Lord of the Flies claims to be "part" of him, Simon looks into the pig's mouth and sees "blackness within, a blackness that spread". The colour black is often used to symbolise evil, so this darkness reflects the idea that evil starts within humans themselves. Additionally, by using the verb "spread", Golding suggests that evil is like a disease which can infect other people.

Answers

Answers

- The way that Simon is murdered suggests that evil acts can be committed out of fear. The noise of the thunder before he stumbles into the boys' ring is "like the blow of a gigantic whip". This violent imagery suggests that the boys are being brutally punished by the weather, making their terror seem justified and explaining why they behave irrationally during Simon's murder. The link between fear and evil might reflect the events of World War Two, during which people sometimes helped the Nazi party to commit horrific crimes out of fear.

2.
- In Chapter Four, Golding suggests that people can use civilised values to gain power. Even though Jack has just acted in an uncivilised way by knocking Piggy's glasses off, the "handsome behaviour" he displays when he apologises earns him the admiration of the hunters. In this way, by exploiting the other boys' respect for civilised values, Jack makes himself seem like a better leader than Ralph. Golding therefore warns the reader that leaders who seem civilised may actually prove to be barbaric.
- Golding adapts the adventure story form to show that humans are less civilised than many people believe. Books such as R. M. Ballantyne's novel, *The Coral Island*, include barbaric figures such as pirates and cannibals, whereas the barbaric characters in Golding's novel are the boys themselves. This reveals his belief that evil exists even inside 'civilised' people. In the 1950s, many people thought that being British was synonymous with being civilised, so this break with tradition may have been particularly surprising and thought-provoking for readers at the time.
- Piggy's commitment to civilised values is used to highlight how these values become irrelevant to most of the other boys. In Chapter Eleven, Piggy wants Jack to know that the conch is "the one thing he hasn't got", even though it is clear that Jack doesn't care about it. Piggy's continued attachment to the conch confirms to the reader how unimportant values such as democracy have become for Jack and his tribe. This is emphasised through the way the imprint of a past assembly in the grass "listened" to Piggy; the use of personification highlights the absence of the boys and suggests that, while their former selves may have listened to and respected others, the boys are now indifferent to their former values.

3.
- Golding uses Ralph's belief that his father will rescue him to hint at the diminished power of the British Navy. When Ralph tries to reason why his father will be able to find them on the island, he gets stuck and is left thinking "because, because". Ralph's inability to complete this sentence suggests that his father has no way of coming to his aid, implying that the Navy is not all-powerful. This reflects the fact that the British Armed Forces were significantly less powerful in the 1950s than they had been previously.
- By writing *Lord of the Flies* in the form of an allegory, Golding uses the novel to reflect the political context of the 1950s. In the novel, Ralph maintains civilised values while Jack chooses savagery. Golding therefore makes the island a microcosm (a small representation) of the whole world, with Ralph symbolising the democratic USA, and Jack symbolising the dictatorship of the USSR. The allegorical nature of the novel would have seemed particularly relevant to readers in the 1950s, when tensions between the USA and the USSR were high and the outbreak of nuclear war was an international concern.
- The way Piggy is presented encourages the reader to think about social class in the 1950s. Piggy's use of non-standard English in expressions such as "Them fruit" suggests that, unlike the other boys, he has not had a privileged education. However, the fact that he remains civilised long after Jack and the choirboys have become barbaric suggests that morality and class are not linked. Golding therefore challenges the widespread belief in the 1950s that people from middle- and upper-class backgrounds were more moral than those from lower social classes.

4.
- The boys' fear of Jack influences their behaviour. In Chapter Twelve, Sam and Eric claim that they "couldn't help" joining Jack's tribe. By this point in the novel, the reader already knows that Jack has punished Wilfred for no reason, making Sam and Eric's unwillingness to challenge Jack seem understandable. This may reflect the way that many ordinary people in Germany in the 1930s joined the Nazi party even though they didn't agree with their ideas because they were afraid of the consequences of not doing so.
- Golding uses the structure of the assemblies to show that the boys' fear is the most important thing to them. In the assemblies in Chapters Two and Five, the discussions about the boys' roles on the island descend into arguments about whether the beast is real. This repeated structure emphasises how the boys' fear of the beast is more of a concern to them than whether they should prioritise hunting or building. The fact that the last assembly before the group splits is all about the beast suggests that by this point, the boys' fear has completely taken over.
- Golding uses the characters' fears to explore their motivations and flaws. For example, in Chapter Five, Ralph "flinched away" from the memory of the littlun who died in the fire. The verb "flinched" suggests that Ralph's natural reflex is to protect himself from pain by not allowing himself to think about his role in the boy's death. Ralph is normally presented as a responsible character, but his fear of acknowledging his failings highlights a weakness in his personality. However, the fact that Ralph silently admits to Piggy that he remembers "the unmentionable" suggests that, despite this weakness, he is fundamentally moral.

5.
- Golding shows that Piggy is a good friend through the way he comforts Ralph. After the group has split, he organises a "feast" to cheer Ralph up. Jack's ability to provide food for the boys is partly what encourages them to join his tribe, so Piggy's use of food to demonstrate to Ralph that they can cope just as well without Jack and the other boys seems thoughtful. Piggy's behaviour may have seemed particularly kind to readers in the 1950s, when food rationing was still part of everyday life and having anything like a "feast" was a rare event for many people.
- Piggy's good treatment of others helps to convey a moral message to the reader. At the end of the novel, Golding structures the list of things that Ralph weeps for so that the sentence leads up to Ralph's memory of the death of the "true, wise friend called Piggy". This gives Piggy's kind nature special emphasis, which suggests that friendship and treating others well is as important as understanding philosophical ideas, such as the "darkness of man's heart". By making Piggy, an outsider, the character the reader should learn from, Golding shows that morality and popularity are not necessarily linked.
- Golding uses Piggy's treatment of others to suggest that kindness can be taken advantage of. In Chapter One, Ralph is generally unkind to Piggy; he betrays Piggy by revealing his nickname, makes fun of his asthma and tells him he is "no good" for exploring the island. By structuring the novel so that the reader has several examples of Ralph making fun of Piggy early on, Golding makes Piggy's consistently good treatment of Ralph seem undeserved. The fact that Ralph recognises Piggy's value by the end of the novel shows how much Ralph matures during his time on the island, partly as a result of Piggy's friendship.

The Characters from 'Lord of the Flies'

Phew! After tackling all those questions, I reckon you deserve a bit of a break. So grab a cup of tea and your favourite kind of biscuit, make yourself comfortable and enjoy *Lord of the Flies — The Cartoon...*

Ralph

Jack

Piggy

Simon

Roger

Sam and Eric

The 'littluns'

The dead airman

The 'Lord of the Flies'

William Golding's 'Lord of the Flies'

ETWL41